ANXIETY MONSTER

HOW TO MANAGE & LIVE WITH ANXIETY

MILTON HARRISON

CONTENTS

Introduction   5

1. Understanding Anxiety and Anxiety Disorders   11
2. A Closer Look at Anxiety Attacks   26
3. Building on Strong Foundations: The Value of a   45
   Healthy Lifestyle
4. Living With Generalized Anxiety Disorder   60
   (GAD)
5. Living With Social Anxiety Disorder   76
6. Living With Obsessive-Compulsive Disorder   93
7. The Power of EFT Tapping in Managing   106
   Anxiety
8. Mindfulness: How to Do It and How It Can   121
   Help You
9. Effective Relaxation Techniques for All Types of   135
   Anxiety
10. Therapy and Medication: What Are Your   150
    Options?

Final Words   163

INTRODUCTION

"You don't have to control your thoughts. You just have to stop letting them control you."

- **Dan Millman**

"You don't have to control your thoughts. You just have to stop letting them control you."

— DAN MILLMAN

When walking down a lonely and dark alley and you notice a towering shadow tailing you, there will definitely be a reaction. Your defense mechanism will be at alert because you will start telling yourself, "What if this person is a robber or, worse, a killer?"

In such a scenario, the "fight or flight" hormone (adrenaline) will be released to help you think faster and act faster to evade the sensed danger. However, there is a side effect of this released adrenaline. It makes you anxious and scared, especially if you feel that person is going to hurt you.

The anxiety you develop in the scenario I just painted is totally normal. In fact, without anxiety, we will be unable to protect ourselves from danger. But as you know, everything has a limit. If your anxiety levels become more than normal, or persistent, or occur when there is little or no danger in sight, they become a problem. In such a case, your anxiety will bring about emotional distress and cause you great discomfort. That can disrupt your life by preventing you from doing the things you ought to do as a human being, such as associating with people, chasing a career, and living a life of freedom.

One can have a stress order and neglect it because they will conclude it is a natural phenomenon. They may feel that what they are experiencing is normal, and every other person gets to feel that way too. In this book, we will see the differences between normal worry and anxiety disorder for clarity's sake. This is important because if you don't identify these disorders for what they are and pursue treatment, they will be with you forever and go from bad to worse.

Anxiety can lead to depression, irrational fears, and even a physical panic, especially when you are in the midst of people. That is when we say that you have allowed your thoughts to control you. Dan Millman, in our opening quote, says it all. The truth is that thoughts will always be haphazard and spontaneous. You may find yourself going over one thought this minute, and the next minute, you will catch yourself grappling with an entirely new thought. That is because you and I cannot have absolute control over our thoughts. What we can do is allow the thoughts to do their things, but control the effect they have on us. If we can achieve that, we can say that we have prevented our thoughts from controlling us.

Over the years, I have gained a sound knowledge of anxiety and several other mental illnesses. I originally specialized in substance abuse, but my interest on how anxiety affects the human mind drove me into areas such as Obsessive-Compulsive Disorder (OCD), Social Anxiety Disorder (SAD), and General Anxiety Disorder (GAD), among several other subjects. In all of these, I have gathered tremendous knowledge and insight. In the course of this book, I will show you everything that my research and practice have taught me.

Why should you read this book? Do you know that anxiety disorders are the most prevalent mental illness in the U.S.? Statistics by Anxiety and Depression Association of America (ADAA) shows that every year, about 40 million adults aged 18 and above in the U.S. suffer from anxiety disorders. That's around 18.1% of the population. So even if you don't have it, there may be somebody you love who does. Even though this disease can be treated, people suffering from it hardly undergo treatment because they erroneously believe it is normal. Statistics say that only 36.9% of people suffering from the illness receive treatment.

The other 73.1% don't undergo treatment. On a worldwide scale, 75% of people who have depression and other mental illnesses in developing countries do not undergo treatment. The sad reality is that people do not realize that they can treat themselves from the comfort of their homes without spending a dime on any specialist. Yes, that is possible, and most of the people that I have taught and treated have been able to manage their anxiety effectively and live normal lives. There are several lifestyles, techniques, and strategies that you can adopt to cope with any anxiety you may have today.

In this book, we will look at the different types of anxiety disorders with an emphasis on the three most common ones —SAD, GAD, and OCD. We will look at the symptoms associated with them, the factors that trigger them, the coping strategies you can adopt, and so on. We will also discuss tested and trusted psychological remedies for them, such as Emotional Freedom Technique (EFT), mindfulness, and relaxation.

As you read this book, you should discover self-care

methods that can help you manage that anxiety you thought was a life sentence. I will provide you with actionable steps that you can follow today to reclaim your freedom. I do not promise you an easy journey because it doesn't exist. At first, you will find it difficult to follow these steps, and it will seem as though it is not working at first, but with sheer determination, desire, and will, you will be amazed by how efficiently you can free yourself from the pangs of anxiety.

The quicker you act, the better for you. Anxiety disorders, just like most other mental illnesses, have a way of deteriorating if they are not treated quickly. Don't make the mistake of concluding that what you have is not an anxiety disorder. If you haven't been diagnosed with the disease, you have information in this book to use to conduct a self-check and know if you have any of these disorders or not. The key thing here is discovering early and acting accordingly before things spiral and depression sets it.

The remedies we will be discussing works because anxiety stems from our thoughts. If that is the case, then something can be done to reduce anxiety if we can work on our thoughts. When a troubling thought next hits your mind, and you catch yourself spiraling into anxiety and panic, know that you can stop those thoughts in their tracks. For instance, mindfulness and relaxation, some of the techniques we will be discussing, will teach you how to be in firm control of your mind by focusing on your present and drawing away from worries that you may have for the future or from a troubled past.

As you read through this book, my promise to you is that I am going to present everything in a language you will understand. I will not bore you with psychological jargon as that will only end up frightening you further. I hope that as you follow the tips and actionable steps I have provided in this book, you will regain your freedom in no time.

You never chose this path for yourself. You didn't just wake up one morning and wish for an anxiety disorder of any sort, but it is here nonetheless. That you have it now is not your fault, but if you choose not to do anything about it even when you can, that's when it becomes your fault.

I hope you make the right call today... See you on the anxiety-free side of life.

1

UNDERSTANDING ANXIETY AND ANXIETY DISORDERS

In the introductory section of this book, we saw how it is okay for us to worry. When, then, should we be bothered, or to what magnitude should it occur before we make a move? In this chapter, we will take an in-depth look at anxiety, and we will also look at the various types of anxiety disorders out there.

My purpose in including this chapter is to help you know for sure if you have an anxiety disorder. For people who might have been diagnosed with the illness, this book will give you a better understanding of the illness you are suffering from. Whatever the case, I want you to realize that this is not a death sentence. It is totally manageable. Several people have done so, and you can do it too.

WHAT, THEN, IS ANXIETY?

Anxiety is a natural human emotion that is a crucial part of the fight or flight response. It can be likened to the alarm system in your house that alerts you when an intruder is on your property. The body's own alarm system is anxiety. It is what tells the body that an "intruder" is nearby. Anxiety and fear have been key to our survival as a species.

It occurs in response to those situations when we anticipate danger or something unpleasant happening. You don't expect the body not to defend itself, do you? Well, this is the first stage of the body defending itself. When anxiety sets in, the body weighs its option. In some cases, it decides to fight, but most times, it settles for flight, which simply means getting as far away as possible from the sensed danger. For instance, in the dark alley example we saw earlier, you have the option of seeing this one out (which is illogical, except maybe if you are a cop looking to catch a street robber), or speed up, or even run to where there are people and sufficient light. The physical responses we experience with anxiety are designed to help us respond to danger, preparing us to flee, fight, or freeze. It is known as the fight or flight response.

So anxiety, when occurring naturally in the right proportion, is not a problem because it is a natural human emotion, more or less like happiness, sadness, and every other human emotion that we express on a daily basis. This one is even a bit more important than other emotions, because thanks to anxiety, you have made it out of several dangerous situations in the past.

Anxiety does not only happen when we are in danger. It also occurs when we are under pressure or when we are faced with a difficult task. This is the reason why interviews, first dates, and public speaking are the greatest enemies that some people will ever know.

In light of this, it becomes obvious that anxiety does not just protect you from danger. Sometimes it serves different purposes, such as keeping you alert and focused, motivating you to solve problems, and spurring you to action.

The following are some of the signs associated with the fight or flight response:

Rapid heart rate & breathing

This is the body's way of preparing you for what is to come. For instance, if you ever fought that bully way back in high school, then you may recall how fast your heart was beating when you had been separated and asked the reason for your fight. My best bet is that you were unable to say a word, or you talked incoherently because you were still struggling to catch your breath.

The increased heart rate ensures that more energy and oxygen are supplied to the crucial body parts so that they can respond swiftly when the danger finally comes.

Pale or flushed skin

The skin becomes pale or flushed because the heart will starve the surface areas of the body blood so that it will supply the brains, muscles, arms, and legs with more blood. The reason is that these parts of the body will be busier when the body engages with the perceived danger. The blood clotting ability of the body also increases so that the body can prevent excessive loss of blood if the body gets injured as it engages with the perceived danger.

Dilated Pupils

Do you know that you see more when your body is in fight or flight mode? For instance, when you get into a fight, the eye becomes better at seeing so that it can watch for an incoming blow and warn you so you can respond suitably.

This is possible because when you are in danger, your pupils dilate to allow more light to get into the eyes. More light transcends to better vision and better response.

Trembling

Trembling occurs because when your body detects danger, it

primes the muscles so that they can react quicker and better. It is this priming that causes shaking or trembling.

WHEN DOES IT BECOME A DISORDER?

When anxiety disrupts our lives and is present constantly, even when there is no genuine reason why it should be there, it has become an anxiety disorder and should be addressed in order to improve your quality of life.

Once anxiety begins to disrupt our life, we are in the territory of an anxiety disorder. That can mess with our stress hormones and fill the mind with toxic thoughts and worries. Such a situation will only push us into an even more anxious state.

As you would expect, there are levels of anxiety disorder. Some sufferers may have chronic anxiety disorders that throw them into fits of panic, so they literally shake when they are anxious. Others might experience a mild case, such as doing everything possible to avoid crowded places or trembling at the mic when it is time to speak before a group of people.

Anxiety disorder is a general label to cover various debilitating conditions. There are seven main ones, three of which will be explored more closely in the book. Some of the disorders are not a single disorder but a group of related conditions.

WHAT CAUSES ANXIETY DISORDERS?

Researchers have not been able to pinpoint a particular thing as the cause of anxiety disorders. For now, the general consensus is that a combination of factors contributes to the disorder. The common factors that have been identified for now are genetics and environmental factors, as well as an individual's brain chemistry.

KEY THINGS YOU SHOULD KNOW ABOUT ANXIETY DISORDER

Recent surveys suggest we live in an "age of anxiety" in which modern life plays a pivotal role and could be responsible for the rise in anxiety disorders.

Research into the parts of the brain involved with anxiety is ongoing.

There is no single test to diagnose an anxiety disorder. Diagnosis involves a long process involving physical examinations, mental health evaluations, and psychological questionnaires.

Anxiety disorders often co-occur with depression, but not always.

Anxiety disorders are a group of interrelated conditions (not a single disorder), and symptoms vary.

Anxiety disorders are some of the most common forms of mental health issues and can be managed with the right information and tools.

WHAT ARE THE LIKELY SYMPTOMS?

You may have an anxiety disorder if:

- You are constantly worried or tense.
- Your anxiety interferes with your work, education, or relationships.
- You can't shake off what you know to be irrational fears.
- You think something bad will happen if things aren't done in a particular way.
- You avoid situations because they cause you anxiety.
- You experience sudden attacks of panic.
- You feel like danger is around every corner.

These symptoms manifest them in two ways: psychological and physical.

The symptoms that are mostly psychological/emotional are:

- Feelings of dread
- Watching for signs of danger
- Expecting the worst
- Difficulty concentrating
- Feeling tense
- Irritability
- Blank mind, especially when before people

The physical ones that are caused by the body being flooded by the stress hormone known as cortisol include:

- Pounding heart
- Sweats
- Headaches
- Stomach ache
- Dizziness
- Shaking or trembling
- Frequent urination or diarrhea.
- Frequent bathroom trips
- Shortness of breath
- Tension in muscles
- Insomnia

Because of the similarity of these symptoms with those of other diseases, sufferers of anxiety disorder usually mistake their illness for other medical illnesses depending on the symptoms that are prevalent. For instance, if a person comes down with a stomach ache and gets diarrhea too, you will need to go the extra mile as a therapist to convince them that it is not diarrhea but an anxiety disorder. This has caused several people with anxiety disorders to truly never notice.

ANXIETY SYMPTOMS AND DEPRESSION

These two are almost becoming synonymous because they are often seen together. If you are suffering from anxiety symptoms, it won't be long before depression sets in. For instance, if you are suffering from a chronic social anxiety disorder, my best bet is that you prefer to lock yourself in your apartment all day long. A condition like that precedes depression because sooner or later, you will start telling yourself that you are not good enough to associate with people. You will convince yourself that you are incomplete, unlike other people. At that stage, depression sets in, and that is when some people cannot handle it anymore, and take their lives.

The presence of depression worsens anxiety symptoms and vice versa.

TYPES OF ANXIETY DISORDER

There are seven types of anxiety disorder. In the course of this book, we will discuss the three most common types of anxiety disorder: SAD, GAD, and OCD. I have dedicated three chapters to them so that we won't be discussing them extensively in this chapter. Discussions on GAD, SAD, and OCD can be found in chapters four, five, and six, respectively. So in this chapter, we will give more attention to those disorders that we may never mention again.

But first, let's remind ourselves of what the three main disorders are:

Generalized Anxiety Disorder (GAD)

This type of anxiety is characterized by worries and fear. It makes you have that persistent feeling that something terrible will happen. If you have noticed that you are a chronic worrywart who always gets this anxious feeling over most things at most times, then you may be suffering from GAD. If you are truly honest with yourself, you will agree with me that most times you don't even know why you are worried. Even when there is a reason, it is hardly substantial enough to elicit such a reaction from you.

This disorder is mostly characterized by symptoms such as restlessness, fatigue, insomnia, and stomach upset.

We will discuss GAD in more detail in chapter four of this book.

Social Anxiety Disorder (SAD)

This order is mostly the fear of socializing with people because you are scared that their view of you might be negative, and you might be humiliated in public. Another name for this disorder is social phobia, which translates to fear of social settings. It is extreme shyness that keeps its sufferers from living their lives to the fullest.

Sufferers prefer to keep to themselves always and associate only when it is inevitable. In extreme cases, the sufferer will withdraw totally from all forms of social gathering. The problem with that is that you need to interact with people to make any headway in life. You need to go to school, be a part of a class, and undertake projects in school before you can graduate. And when you do, you need to take up a job and communicate with your coworkers. Even if you are starting your digital business from your home, at some point you will need to make presentations. You need to relieve yourself of some stress by spending quality time with family or friends. But with SAD, all of these things will elude you.

SAD will be discussed in more detail in chapter five.

. . .

Obsessive-Compulsive Disorder (OCD)

This disorder is characterized by recurring irrational thoughts that can cause the sufferer to perform specific behaviors in a repetitive manner. It also causes undesired behaviors and thoughts that you cannot control. In extreme cases, a sufferer may experience uncontrollable compulsions like washing their face time and time again without any need for such actions. In some people, it is a recurring worry that they have left something undone that needed to be done. For instance, a sufferer may erroneously believe that they left their door open on their way out of the house earlier that day when, in fact, they locked up everywhere accordingly.

OCD will be discussed in more detail in chapter six.

Panic Disorder

Panic disorder, also known as a panic attack, is characterized by sudden, repeated panic attacks and the fear of experiencing the attack again. This fear of experiencing the attack again can be more debilitating than the actual attack itself. Panic disorder is often associated with agoraphobia, which is the fear of being in a place where it might be difficult to escape or get help in a difficult event. People with agoraphobia will avoid confined spaces such as airplanes.

PHOBIAS AND IRRATIONAL FEARS

These are characterized by an exaggerated and intense fear of specific things, places, or situations. This fear is termed irrational because, oftentimes, the actual danger is way less than what the sufferer senses it to be.

Some of the most common phobias are fear of animals, heights, enclosed space, or flying. Sufferers of these phobias will do everything possible to avoid those things they are scared of. The result is a continual and increasing fear of that thing. Before the sufferer can overcome their fears, they must face their fears and see for themselves that they had been exaggerating.

My guess is that you never thought phobias were mental illnesses. Well, now you know. So if you have one of those misplaced fears, it is time to rid yourself of it.

Post-Traumatic Stress Disorder (PTSD)

This is an extreme anxiety disorder that is the result of traumatic events in the life of the sufferer. It can also be caused by life-threatening situations in which the sufferer never thought they would survive. When the traumatic or life-threatening situation is gone, the sufferer is not able to erase it from their mind. So it remains there and torments them until they do something about it.

It is a condition that is very common with war veterans because they had seen horrible things when they were fighting in wars. They are never able to erase these terrible memories, and it manifests itself as PTSD.

The common systems are nightmares, hypervigilance, quick startling, flashbacks, and a strong desire to avoid situations that can remind the sufferer of the memories that haunts them.

Separation Anxiety Disorder

This disorder is most common in children. It is normal for children not to want to be separated from their parents, but if the anxiety associated with the separation intensifies, it becomes a problem. If you notice that your child becomes agitated at the thought of being separated from you, they may have a separation anxiety disorder.

In summary, anxiety, when occurring moderately and naturally, is good. And you must learn to pay close attention whenever you catch yourself feeling anxious. But if it becomes too much that it now interferes with your activities and wellbeing, you must seek a solution. There are no carved-in-stone symptoms for any of the anxiety disorders. So your symptoms might be different from those of your neighbor with the same condition. That is because anxiety disorders are mostly a combination of several disorders, not just one.

Later in this book, I will show you several self-care routines that you can adopt in your fight against anxiety disorders. It is totally curable. The key thing is getting to know what your disorders are. And do not go hard on yourself for having any anxiety disorders. Realize that you are not alone; so many others have it and are living life as they should, so do not limit yourself from achieving what you are able.

2

A CLOSER LOOK AT ANXIETY ATTACKS

We often confuse panic attacks with anxiety attacks, but there are differences between them. The two main reasons they are mistaken for each other is that anxiety attacks aren't medically recognized, and panic attacks are often experienced by those living with anxiety.

I will explain how they are related, so you have a better understanding.

ANXIETY ATTACK AND PANIC ATTACK, HOW DO THEY RELATE?

In my years of practice, I've seen people use anxiety attacks and panic attacks interchangeably. They just assume they are alternate names for a single disorder. But that is not the case because even though they have their similarities, they have significant differences.

The main reason why people tend to mistake them for each other is that they share some common symptoms, and these symptoms can be experienced simultaneously or concurrently. For instance, worrying about a stressful meeting can cause anxiety, which may culminate as a panic attack during the meeting. In this case, we see how it is possible for one attack to stem from another one.

People who experience anxiety attacks are more likely to have panic attacks. But that doesn't mean that everybody with an anxiety disorder will get a panic disorder. It is possible to live with an anxiety disorder and never experience a panic attack.

It may be that if you live with an anxiety disorder, panic attacks are part of your experience. They usually peak within ten minutes and last less than 30 minutes. They can be very frightening, sometimes with symptoms so severe that they feel like a heart attack.

PANIC ATTACKS

Panic attacks can be destabilizing for its sufferer. When it occurs, you will be scared because you will feel like you are losing control or going crazy. In extreme cases, you may even conclude that you have a heart attack that may kill you. But on its own, a panic attack is not life-threatening.

If you experience a panic attack once or twice in a lifetime, it doesn't mean that you have panic disorder. Many people will experience the occasional panic attack, but this doesn't mean they have panic disorder. It only becomes a panic disorder when the panic attack is recurrent, and you notice that you are living in fear that you might experience another attack shortly. It is this fear that is even more damaging because you will do all you can to avoid situations that you feel may lead to another attack. This has caused several people living with panic disorder to avoid work, school, and other social gatherings. With such a routine, it becomes very difficult for the individual to reach their true potential in life.

A panic attack can occur anywhere or at any time without warning. It can happen when you are fast asleep, at work, driving, or at the mall. It is believed that when a particular event causes you to have a panic attack, that event has a way of making you feel endangered and trapped. When your mind has set itself on this belief even when it might not be true, it causes your body to go into the fight or flight mode. (We discussed the fight and flight mode earlier.) As your body enters that mode, it manifests most of the responses that your body would normally manifest when it is in actual danger.

There are several variations in symptoms. This means that the symptoms you will get, and their duration will differ from that of someone else. Irrespective of the variations, the attack and resultant symptoms usually peak within minutes. After you recover from the panic attack, you may feel exhausted, as though you just did a tedious task.

The intense fear you feel during the attack can mar your self-confidence and disrupt your everyday life, depending on the intensity of the attack. It can cause the following panic disorder symptoms:

- Anticipatory Anxiety: This is the constant fear you have in-between episodes that prevent you from being your normal self, even when the panic is not upon you. It affects your efficiency at every other thing because it can be disabling.
- Phobic Avoidance: This is the name for the avoidance I talked about. You may believe that the situation you are avoiding was the cause of your previous attack. Hence, you will do everything you can to never be in that condition again.

HOW TO OVERCOME FEAR OF PANIC ATTACK

In your attempt to reduce panic attack episodes, you will need to have a strong answer to anticipatory anxiety that we discussed above. Again, it is the way you respond to the unpleasant situation that determines the extent to which the panic attack will affect you.

Most people react to the unpleasant situation by convincing themselves that they cannot control themselves, or that they are having a heart attack. Some people will even conclude that they are going insane or, in the worst-case scenario, that they are dying. All of these conclusions will just escalate the fear in them and cause symptoms to increase until they get out of hand.

You can overcome your fear by:

1. Educating yourself

By reading this book, you are already doing some of what is necessary. It is better when you recognize panic disorder for what it is because that will eliminate some of the misplaced fear such as, "I am going to die," or "I am going insane" that people usually have when they have panic attacks. You should eliminate these fears because they always escalate your symptoms.

As you educate yourself and recognize the likely symptoms, you will identify them for what they truly are.

2. Don't live in denial

After educating yourself, accept your panic attacks. Don't try to resist the symptoms as that can worsen your situation by increasing your fear and anxiety. The idea here is that when you accept your panic attacks, you will alter your perception of the attacks. That is when you can cope because you begin to see it as a natural phenomenon, and not a curse that has come to ruin you.

3. Change your response

When you have accepted your panic attacks, the next thing you should change is the response you give to panic attacks. Instead of responding with fear, anxiety, and negative beliefs, start to respond with calmness, clarity, and control.

These three responses can be regarded as the Three A's: Acknowledge, Accept, and give Alternative responses. In the acknowledgment stage of this process, you are expected to be calm and recognize the experience. In the acceptance, try to come to terms with the fact that you are in the middle of a panic attack. Finally, in the alternative response, tell yourself that the feelings you are experiencing are just temporary.

SOME CHARACTERISTICS OF PANIC ATTACK

- It comes on suddenly and involves intense/overwhelming fear.
- It comes with physical symptoms such as a racing heart, shortness of breath, or nausea.
- It is recognized by the Diagnostic and Statistical Manual of Mental Disorders (DSM-5).
- It may not always be cued by stressors—it may come out of the blue. But expected panic attacks are cued by external stressors, such as phobias.
- Severe, disruptive symptoms—fight or flight response—takes over.
- It often triggers fears related to having another attack.

SOME CHARACTERISTICS OF ANXIETY ATTACKS:

- Aren't recognized by the DSM-5
- May come on gradually.
- Lack of diagnostic recognition makes them harder to define by symptoms.

- It is typically related to something perceived as stressful.
- It can be mild, moderate, or severe, and builds gradually.

DIFFERENCES BETWEEN ANXIETY ATTACK AND PANIC ATTACK

The differences between the symptoms of an anxiety attack and panic attack can be classified into emotional and physical.

Emotional:

An anxiety attack is characterized by apprehension and worry, distress, restlessness, and fear, while a panic attack is characterized by fear. This may include fear of dying or losing control, or a sense of detachment from the world.

Physical:

In terms of physical symptoms, there is hardly a clear difference between them. The only difference is in the severity, with a panic attack generally being more severe. The physical symptoms are explained in the next section.

SYMPTOMS OF PANIC ATTACK

A panic disorder showcases itself in the form of a panic attack. The symptoms associated with a panic attack can cut across the physical, emotional, and cognitive aspects of a patient.

If you have experienced the following, you may have had a panic attack:

Heart palpitations.

Heart palpitation is one of the greatest sources of fear for people experiencing panic attacks. They will erroneously believe that the accelerated heart rate they are experiencing is caused by either a heart attack or other medical emergencies.

But that is not the case. An accelerated heart rate can occur due to several reasons, such as excitement and natural nervousness. When your heart beats fast due to excitement, you are calm and collected, but when it happens during a panic attack, you interpret it as a heart attack, and that is the problem.

As we will see later in this book, simple exercises, such as deep breathing, can put you back in control.

Shaking.

During a panic attack, you may experience trembling sensations, which will show as shaky legs, arms, hands, and feet. This can really frighten you, but on closer inspection, you will realize that these are normal body reactions to fight or flight mode.

Excessive Sweating.

The sweating you experience is caused by the anxious feeling that you are having. It is the way our body responds to stress. If you didn't know this, you could interpret it to mean a very serious emergency.

This sweating may be accompanied by chills or hot flashes. It may be hot sweat or cold sweat. Whichever way it comes, realize that it is just the body's way of responding to stress.

Hyperventilation.

During a panic attack, you may not be able to breathe the way you do when you are calm. You may notice that instead of having calm, rhythmic breathing, you take quick, short breaths. It can be really frightening because you can feel like you're about to choke.

Apart from these major symptoms, other common ones are:

- Feeling faint
- Trouble breathing
- Hot flashes or chills
- Overwhelming panic
- Loss of control
- Nausea
- Feeling detached

Risk factors include:

- Experiencing or witnessing trauma in the past
- Experiencing a stressful life event
- Ongoing stress and worry
- Living with a chronic health condition
- Having another mental health disorder
- Substance use
- Anxiety or panic disorders in the family

TYPES OF PANIC ATTACK

Not everybody who suffers a panic attack experiences the same type of attack. The symptoms associated with the different types of attacks may be similar, but the causes will differ.

The three recognized type of panic attacks are:

1. Unexpected (Un-cued) Panic Attacks

These types of attacks come upon the sufferer without any signal, warning, or trigger. It is a rapid attack that seems to come out of thin air. If you suffer from an unexpected panic attack, you may go into a full state of panic without any clear cause. You may not be doing anything that could lead to an attack, yet, it will still arise. Due to its nature, this type of attack cannot be predicted; neither can you prepare for it. Since this attack occurs without any situational or environmental trigger, it can even happen while you are asleep.

At the time of the attack, patients will normally experience symptoms such as a rapid heartbeat or rise in body temperature and may feel the need to leave where they are at the time of the attack.

2. Situational Bound or Cued Panic Attacks:

This type of attack occurs when you are exposed to certain situations. Once you have suffered a panic attack over a situation, that situation is likely to become a cue or trigger for subsequent panic episodes. For instance, if you have a fear of social gatherings, and it has led you to a panic attack before, you may suffer another episode when you are in a social gathering. You may also suffer an attack just by thinking about a social gathering. For you, work meetings, family gatherings, interviews, religious gatherings, and parties become a no-no because you know it can trigger another episode.

Due to their nature, they are more predictable. But this predictability itself is a demerit to you because when you are aware that you might suffer a panic attack, the chances of it happening will increase. That is because the fear and anxiety you have that it may happen can be extremely overwhelming, and you can only hold in there for so long before you give in to the tension.

3. Situationally Predisposed Panic Attacks:

This type of attack is actually caused by triggers, but the attack does not occur immediately upon exposure. It will lead to delayed attack, happening after you have been exposed to the trigger several times. This means that a person with a social anxiety disorder may not experience a panic disorder at a social gathering, but upon continuous exposure or after leaving the social gathering, they may suffer an attack.

For instance, if somebody's trigger for an attack is flying, they may not experience an attack while they are flying, but when they get off the plane or even get home, they may have a panic attack.

This type of attack is a bit more complex than the others

because a panic attack might or might not occur on exposure to triggers.

CAUSES OF PANIC ATTACK

As at the time of writing this book, the medical world has not been able to clearly identify the exact cause of panic attacks and panic disorders. However, it is believed that it can be hereditary.

The items listed below are the possible causes of expected panic attacks since the unexpected ones don't have external triggers. Also, note that these causes can also trigger an anxiety attack. The triggers are:

- Stressful tasks, such as tough jobs.
- Driving.
- Social situations.
- Phobias such as claustrophobia or agoraphobia.
- Memories of past traumatic experiences.
- Chronic illnesses, such as heart diseases, diabetes, and asthma.
- Chronic pain.
- Caffeine (I will show you how this can trigger a panic attack in chapter three when we start discussing lifestyle changes you should try).
- Medication and supplements.

- Thyroid problems.

Apart from the causes above, panic attacks can also be caused by medical conditions.

DIAGNOSIS

Doctors cannot diagnose anxiety attacks, but panic attacks, alongside anxiety symptoms, anxiety disorders, and panic disorders can be diagnosed. Before diagnosis, the doctor will ask you what symptoms you've noticed. If these are in line with some of the symptoms we've identified above, the doctor will conduct other tests to rule out the possibility that your symptoms are due to illnesses other than a panic attack. For instance, heart diseases and thyroid problems have some symptoms that are similar to panic attack symptoms.

To be sure it is really a panic disorder, you may have to see a doctor who will conduct relevant tests to rule out the following possibilities:

1. Mitral valve prolapses. This is a minor cardiac problem that is a result of the inefficiency of one of the heart valves.
2. Hyperthyroidism. This is a medical condition that is caused by an overactive thyroid gland.

3. Hyperglycemia. This is a condition caused by low blood sugar.

The usual tests that you would expect a doctor to perform are a physical examination, blood tests, a psychological evaluation, and heart tests such as an electrocardiogram (ECG or EKG).

Whatever the result of your analysis, don't panic over it. Know that there are several home remedies that can reduce or stop the symptoms altogether. We will discuss them in subsequent chapters. Keep reading to discover them.

DEALING WITH AN ANXIETY OR PANIC ATTACK

- Take slow, deep breaths, focusing your attention on every breath. Count to four as you exhale, and repeat until breathing slows.
- Recognize and accept the attack. Remind yourself that it will pass.
- Practice mindfulness. This will be discussed in detail in chapter eight of this book.
- Use relaxation techniques. In chapter nine of this book, we will discuss this in detail.

We will discuss these coping strategies later in this book.

Prevention

It may not be feasible to prevent attacks completely, but you can reduce the severity and frequency by:

- Reducing or taking out the sources of stress in your life.
- Learning to identify and stop negative thoughts.
- Practice meditation.
- Join a support group.
- Make lifestyle changes. Lifestyle changes such as exercising, eating healthy, and sleeping correctly, are some lifestyle changes that can help improve your condition. (We will talk more on this in chapter 3.)

Medication

While a panic attack itself cannot be treated with medication, some of the associated symptoms can. So a doctor might recommend medication for these treatable symptoms.

The common medications for panic disorder symptoms are:

Antidepressants: This medication works best when a person living with panic disorder is also experiencing symptoms of depression. The common antidepressants are serotonin reuptake inhibitors (SSRI) such as Prozac (fluoxetine) and Zoloft (sertraline).

Anti-anxiety medications: This medication may ease anxiety by acting as a depressant on the central nervous system. Common examples are benzodiazepines, such as Xanax.

LONG-TERM OUTLOOK

Unfortunately, panic disorder is a long-term condition, and it may be challenging to treat. While some people with this illness may react to medical treatments, most won't. Those who respond may enter a period of no symptoms, but they can spiral into periods of intense symptoms. However, changes in diet, sleeping patterns, and relaxation techniques can help. I will show you how.

Summarily, anxiety attacks and panic attacks are not the same as most people think. One of the significant differences is that while a panic attack is identified in DSM-5 as a mental disorder, an anxiety attack is not. While the two ailments share similar symptoms, triggers, and risk factors, panic attacks tend to be more intense and can bring severe physical symptoms with it, unlike anxiety attacks.

Whatever your condition may be, I want you to find solace in the fact that they both can be treated. Irrespective of what the cause may be and the way it manifests itself, you can gradually eliminate the symptoms of the panic so you can regain your confidence and live your best life.

In the next chapter, we will be going deeper as I will be introducing the value of a healthy lifestyle.

3

BUILDING ON STRONG FOUNDATIONS: THE VALUE OF A HEALTHY LIFESTYLE

In the fight against every form of anxiety, having a strong foundation is an excellent place to start. Having a strong foundation means you are living a healthy lifestyle. In this chapter, I will show you all the great ways you can reduce anxiety by living a healthy life. I will not just show you what you have to do; I will also show you the benefits you can get from doing them.

Lifestyle changes may not completely cure an anxiety disorder. Still, if you live with anxiety, you can make changes to your diet, your exercise routine, sleep, and social patterns that can help reduce symptoms and help you manage your anxiety on the day-to-day. Ensuring your lifestyle is healthy and balanced across all of these elements can give you a strong foundation on which to build other factors to reduce anxiety.

Whether you have an anxiety disorder or you live with milder or less persistent anxiety, lifestyle changes can help improve your symptoms. If you lead an unhealthy lifestyle, you are more likely to experience anxiety.

Now let's see some of your life areas that you can tweak today to help you overcome anxiety disorder no matter the form it takes.

DIET

There are indications that some foods can help reduce the symptoms of anxiety, and some can increase anxiety and intensify physical symptoms.

For instance, alcohol and caffeine are notoriously bad for anxiety patients, likewise fatty foods. When you reduce your fatty foods intake and take enough calcium, zinc, a lot of fresh foods such as vegetables, and plenty of water, it will help reduce the symptoms. Many other dietary options can help in relieving anxiety, and we will discuss them extensively in this chapter.

At the basic level, a balanced diet and staying hydrated can help relieve anxiety, but specific diets can do even more for you in your fight against anxiety. They include:

. . .

1. Complex carbohydrates

Complex carbohydrates are metabolized slowly during digestion, and that can help you stabilize your blood sugar level,
which creates a calmer feeling. Complex carbohydrates
include fruits, whole grains, and vegetables. A diet rich in
whole grain, vegetables, and fruits is healthier and recommended rather than eating simple carbohydrates found in
processed foods. That means fast foods and junks may not be
the right call at this point in your life because they lack
complex carbohydrates. Stick to the ones mentioned here or
have a nutritionist plan your meal to afford you more
complex carbohydrates daily.

2. Foods that Prompt The Release of Neurotrans-
mitters:

Certain foods are even more important for people with
anxiety disorders. For instance, the following foods prompt
the release of neurotransmitters (e.g., serotonin and
dopamine), which can improve anxiety symptoms.

Probiotics

Probiotics are important because they improve gut health.
That is because the gut-brain axis, the lining precisely,
contains 95% of serotonin receptors. Examples of probiotics
are pickles, kefir, and yogurt.

Foods with a high magnesium content

Magnesium is a crucial mineral in the body. It plays an important role in many bodily functions, along with other health benefits. It is very helpful as a natural treatment for anxiety. In an experiment designed to learn more about the relationship between magnesium and anxiety, diets low in magnesium caused test mice to exhibit more anxiety-related behaviors. It was concluded that foods rich in magnesium could induce feelings of calmness in both mice and humans. One of the reasons why magnesium might reduce anxiety is that it can improve brain function. It does that by regulating neurotransmitters, which send messages throughout the body. Magnesium also improves brain functions that reduce stress and anxiety. It is a part of the brain called the hypothalamus. The hypothalamus regulates the pituitary and adrenal glands, which controls the body's response to stress. These are all reasons why you need to have enough magnesium in your diet. Examples of foods rich in magnesium are leafy greens, legumes, nuts and seeds, and whole grains.

Foods high in zinc:

Zinc is an important mineral that aids in cell development and expression of genes. Many people misunderstand the importance of zinc in mental health disorders. The body needs zinc to make neurotransmitters, and without zinc, a neurotransmitter imbalance can cause symptoms of anxiety.

It is important we take a proper balance of neurotransmitters such as GABA, norepinephrine, dopamine, and serotonin. The neurotransmitter that affects mood, appetite, sleep, digestion, libido, and memory is primarily serotonin. Norepinephrine is a stress hormone. It is released from the sympathetic nervous system in response to stress. GABA is connected to anxiety. Dopamine is mostly found in the brain and affects your emotions, sensations of pleasure and pain, and movement. So it is necessary to take foods high in zinc such as cashews, liver, oysters, beef, and egg yolks. Foods having omega-3 fatty acids such as salmon and mackerel also have good zinc content and can help reduce anxiety symptoms.

Foods high in B vitamins

Foods containing B vitamins are essential when trying to reduce anxiety levels. That is because Vitamin B helps balance blood sugar levels, which is a significant factor in controlling anxiety. Vitamin B is grouped into eight separate vitamins, and each is essential. Vitamin B5 helps the adrenal glands that reduce anxiety levels and stress. Vitamin B12 and vitamin B9 are needed for reducing depression. Vitamin B6 and magnesium can both help reduce anxiety. Vitamin B3 helps in the synthesis of serotonin and has been shown to help with anxiety. Foods high in vitamin B include avocados, bananas, potatoes, liver, nutritional yeast, and almonds.

Asparagus

Asparagus has anti-anxiety properties. Asparagus is rich in fiber, potassium, and vitamins A, C, E, and K, and its beneficial trace is well-known to reduce anxiety. It is also known as a mood enhancer. It is so effective against anxiety that the Chinese government approved it for use in beverages.

3. Foods High in Antioxidants

Research shows that anxiety is caused when a body has a lowered antioxidant state, increasing foods high in antioxidants can help. A 2010 study showed the antioxidant content of 3,100 supplements, beverages, spices, herbs, and foods. That study was conducted because it is common knowledge that antioxidants can reduce the risk of oxidative stress-related diseases.

The United States Department of Agriculture (USDA) stipulates that the foods listed below are high in antioxidant content:

- Beans such as red kidney, black, pinto, and small dried red.
- Fruits such as apples, prunes, sweet cherries, and black plums.
- Berries such as strawberries, blackberries, cranberries, raspberries, and blueberries.

- Nuts such as walnuts and pecans.
- Vegetables such as spinach, beet, broccoli, and kale.

Foods alone will not eliminate your anxiety disorder, but there is growing evidence that shows a strong connection between nutrition and psychiatry. Studies are still ongoing, but from what we see already, the future linking healthy foods and healthy minds is positive.

Meal timing

The diets recommended above can be more effective for you if you don't skip meals. When you skip meals, your blood sugar may drop, and this can cause you to feel jittery, worsening any underlying anxiety. It can have other consequences, which also increase anxiety. For instance, complex carbohydrates stabilize your blood sugar but ask yourself what will happen if you have a meal rich in carbohydrates, but you skipped breakfast and lunch.

In essence, the meals mentioned are most efficient when you are consistent with them.

THINGS TO AVOID

Just as some food items can help relieve your symptoms, there are some that you should try to minimize because they can worsen your condition. Cutting certain foods out altogether can also be beneficial.

Let's look at some of the things you should reduce or cut out entirely from your diet so that you can further reduce your anxiety episodes and the severity of the symptoms you will suffer in the once-in-a-while episodes.

Caffeine

If you are a lover of coffee, I know this point will not appeal to you. Some people have told me how they will want to try every other thing I have recommended, but not this one. But the truth is, you have no other choice but to cut down or totally forgo those coffee breaks. Excessive consumption of caffeine can trigger anxiety and aggravate symptoms; it does this by increasing the activity around the sympathetic nervous system. Also, caffeine is known to be a stimulant and can worsen an anxious patient's condition by triggering an anxiety attack. When someone with anxiety takes caffeine, it blocks the adenosine that makes you feel tired and triggers the release of adrenaline that increases energy, thereby keeping you in the "fight or flight" mode we talked about earlier.

Do you know that if you consume over 200 mg of caffeine, this can increase your likelihood of having a panic or anxiety attack? Excessive consumption of caffeine has also been shown to result in symptoms ranging from symptoms of General Anxiety Disorder (GAD) to phobic, and obsessive-compulsive symptoms.

Coffee is not the only food that has high caffeine content. Other foods and drinks that may have high caffeine content are sodas, candies, coffee liqueurs, green tea, dark chocolate, and energy drinks.

Withdrawal symptoms of caffeine: If caffeine is a big part of your diet, stopping it at once could have a bad effect on you in the short-term. The effects that you might encounter include sleepiness, tiredness, headache, down moods, difficulty in concentration, and so on. These symptoms might start within two or three days from when you stopped taking it. So you should stop it gradually by reducing the quantity bit by bit until you are used to not taking it.

But if you must take it, keep it as minimal as possible. To avoid the negative effects of caffeine on your health, you should consume one 12-ounce coffee or one shot of espresso (about 350mg a day) daily, nothing more than that.

Timing matters too. Taking coffee in the dead of night is all shades of wrong. Some people ignorantly harm themselves by drinking caffeine at 12:00 pm. Taking caffeine by this time or beyond can cause severe harm to your health and increase your anxiety level. So it is advised not to take caffeine after midday.

Excessive Sugar

Sugar can contribute to low energy levels, nervousness, sleep disturbance, and increased anxiety. Diet with a high amount of sugar easily zaps the energy level instead of boosting them. And at the same, it also increases your craving for a diet that is sugary, which takes you through the energy-draining circle.

Monosodium Glutamate (MSG)

This salt has been shown to affect most people by increasing their chances of getting an anxiety attack. How does it affect us? It does this by depleting the essential potassium in our system. Functionally, potassium is vital because it helps the nervous system to function properly, but monosodium glutamate uses the supply of potassium in the body. That increases blood pressure and strains the heart and arteries. This increased blood pressure can provoke the nervous system causing chest pain, headache, sleeplessness, and numbness, all of which are symptoms of anxiety. Their occurrence can even trigger an attack.

Alcohol

Alcohol can also worsen symptoms, and if it is used to self-medicate, it can lead to dependency issues. Alcohol changes the level of serotonin and other neurotransmitters in the brain, and that can worsen anxiety in an anxious person. In fact, a person with anxiety may feel more anxious after the alcohol wears off. This anxiety that returns after the alcohol wears off may last even longer.

Away from what to eat and what not to eat, let's look at other lifestyle changes that can be very efficient in the fight against anxiety disorders.

1. Exercise:

You must have heard that regular exercise is good for your health. Some people erroneously believe that health has to do with the physical body alone. But in the actual sense, a person is said to be healthy if they have a sound mind and body. So yes, exercising also improves the mind and helps relieve the illnesses that attack the mind, such as anxiety disorders. Exercise helps to relieve anxiety naturally because exercise is important for maintaining mental fitness, and it also helps reduce stress. It eases anxiety because it causes your body to release the feel-good hormones (endorphins), which lifts your mood. This is the reason why you feel elated just after exercising.

The best form of exercises for an anxiety disorder should be done as stipulated below:

- Aim for at least 30 minutes of aerobic exercise most days.
- Rhythmic activities that involve both arms and legs are effective—walking, running, swimming, dancing, etc.
- Maintaining a regular exercise routine associated with improved moves leads to better self-esteem and increased energy.

Such exercises can reduce the body's physical reaction to anxiety and the frequency/intensity of panic attacks. It can also help the body in releasing tension. Researchers have found that even a short brisk walk can provide several hours of relief. That is why physically active people have lower rates of anxiety than sedentary people. Exercise also helps the brain to cope with stress.

2. Stress reduction:

When we were discussing anxiety and panic disorders, we identified stress as one of the factors that can cause or contribute to those disorders. Since that is the case, it is only logical for you to look for a way to either eliminate the stress or manage it in such a way that it will not have too much impact on your mental health.

Chapter nine of this book will show you some stress

management techniques that can help you cope with daily stressors that you cannot eliminate.

But before we discuss that, take a critical look at your daily routine today and start identifying those things that cause you stress. Once you have identified them, ask yourself, "can I eliminate this, or is it something I will have to put up with?" If you have to put up with it, see if there is a way you can reduce them. Oftentimes, there are ways you can cut down on those stressful tasks. For instance, look at your responsibilities and see if you can delegate them to others.

3. Sleep

I am sure you have heard that improper or insufficient sleep is harmful to your mind and body, but do you also know that lack of sleep can exacerbate anxious feelings? If you didn't know, well, now you do. The reason is that neurotransmitters that your body needs to support your moods are replenished when you are sleeping.

This is why you need to aim for 7–9 hours of quality sleep every night. I know that a lot is being said about hard workers who sacrifice their sleep for goals. You can work hard and achieve great things and still get sufficient sleep at night. It all boils down to efficient planning and timing.

And the fact that you have issues with anxiety further makes it very important for you of all people.

Research has found that people who deprive themselves of sleep are more likely to classify neutral images as negative. Everyday items can seem more menacing and contribute to anxiety. Anxiety can make it even more difficult for you to sleep.

If you're struggling to improve sleep quality or quantity, the following can help:

- Meditation.
- Exercise.
- Prioritization of to-do list.
- Listening to calming music.
- Removal of distractions such as turning off devices an hour before bed.
- Your sleeping environment should also be a calming space, with a moderated temperature of between 60 and 67 degrees Fahrenheit.
- Comfortable mattress and pillows make sleeping easier and better.

4. Social

If your anxiety isn't social anxiety disorder (SAD), this point will be lots easier for you. But if you are battling with SAD, chapter 5 will show you how you can manage to beat your fears and socialize more.

Loneliness and isolation can exacerbate anxiety symptoms because when you talk about your anxiety with people, this can make it less overwhelming. Try to see friends, relatives, coworkers, neighbors, and fellow worshippers whenever the need arises. Never shy away from it because if you do, you will be further validating the anxieties you have about yourself.

Another less socializing thing you can do is join support groups where you can hear from other people like you, and what they did or are doing to help their case. They could be your support network and look out for you when you are losing it.

You can also get yourself a lovely pet because your pet's company can help you too. Rather than focusing on yourself and your problems, you can focus your attention on caring for your pet and creating a great relationship with it.

In conclusion, all of the tips we have discussed in this chapter will only be effective if you quit chronic worrying. It is a mental habit that keeps you on edge every time. But the good news is that you can break it just like every other mental habit.

4

LIVING WITH GENERALIZED ANXIETY DISORDER (GAD)

G AD is one of the most common anxiety disorders. It can significantly impact your life by creating emotional, behavioral, and physical symptoms. It is usual for someone to feel anxious sometimes. But it is a cause for concern if your fears and worries become constant and, as a result, hinder your body and soul from functioning and relaxing. Strategies to help you cope include social strategies, self-soothing, reframing your worries, and learning your triggers. While these approaches may not wholly cure GAD, they can make it much easier to live with.

GAD is diagnosed when your anxiety is so constant that it ends up interfering with your daily life. On more days than not, you may find it difficult to have control over worry for at least six months and have three or more of the symptoms discussed in this chapter.

Common anxiety disorders involve constant/chronic worrying, nervousness, and tension—not focused on one specific situation or thing. A person with a phobia has a fear that is connected to a particular thing or situation, which is entirely not the case with GAD. A person suffering from GAD has a diffused form of fear; they have a general feeling of unease that colours their whole life.

The anxiety related to GAD is usually less intense than a panic attack, but it tends to last longer. For panic attack, the feeling of fear occurs suddenly, and it is intense and tends to cause more harm to the person.

In the US, GAD affects 3.1% of the population and about 6.8 million adults in any given year. Women are twice as more susceptible to GAD than men. This type of anxiety comes on gradually and can begin across the life cycle. The risk is at its worst between childhood and middle age. The exact cause of GAD is unknown; however, there is evidence that family background, biological factors, and life experiences, especially stressful ones, plays a role.

A person with GAD may worry about similar things to other people but at a more intense level. For instance, a careless comment from a co-worker about the company's bad economy becomes a vision of imminent official notice that you have been fired from your job; a delayed response from a friend to a call or email leads to anxiety the relationship is coming to an end. Most times, even the thought of getting through the day develops anxiety. People with GAD have a form of exaggerated worry or tension as they go about their activities. This is the case even when there is little or nothing to worry about. They find it very difficult or even impossible to turn off their anxious thoughts, even when they know that their anxiety or worry is more intense than the situation warrants and try to stop it. They usually think this worry is beyond their control.

People with GAD, whose anxiety level is mild to moderate or with treatment, can have full and meaningful lives, be gainfully employed, and function socially. But people with GAD must avoid situations that may trigger anxiety. They should try not to take advantage of opportunities due to their worry (travel, promotions, social situations, etc.). Many have trouble carrying out the simplest daily activities when their anxiety level is high.

THE DIFFERENCE BETWEEN GAD AND "NORMAL" WORRY

It is a normal part of life for you to have doubts, worries, and fears. It is also natural to be anxious about a future event or situation, such as an upcoming exam, or a delayed funds transaction into your account. The difference between GAD and "normal" worrying is that the worries emanated from

GAD are usually excessive, disruptive, persistent, and intrusive.

The difference between Generalized Anxiety Disorder (GAD) and "Normal" Worry

Generalized Anxiety Disorder:	"Normal" Worry
It hinders your activities, job, or social life.	It doesn't hinder your daily responsibilities and activities.
It is uncontrollable	It is controllable
It is extremely stressful and upsetting.	It may be unpleasant, but it doesn't lead to significant distress.
It emanates from all sorts of things, expecting the worst from each.	It is limited to a particular, small case of realistic concerns.
This form of worry exists for at least six months. almost	This form of worry lasts for only a short period of time.

SYMPTOMS OF GENERALIZED ANXIETY DISORDER (GAD)

The symptoms of GAD can differ from person to person depending on several factors such as biological factors, and life experiences. In this section of our investigation of living with GAD, we will discuss the emotional, behavioral, and physical symptoms of GAD.

Emotional:

- You are constantly worried about things and situations, even about the situations beyond your control and those that don't call for worry. The worrying associated with GAD is disproportionate to the situations that trigger it.

- Over time, you will develop a feeling that your anxiety is uncontrollable, and may end up giving in to it by concluding that there is nothing you can do to prevent or stop the worrying.

- Most often, you are faced with intrusive thoughts about the things and situations that make you anxious. Although you may try to stop thinking about them, you can't.

- You have an inability to tolerate uncertainty; you feel you need to know what is going to happen beforehand.

- A pervasive feeling of apprehension always confronts you.

Behavioral

- You are always unable to relax, be by yourself, or enjoy the quiet time because you are confronted by a sense of impending danger, doom, or panic. Although restlessness doesn't occur in all people with GAD, it is one of the red flags doctors frequently look out for during diagnosis. If you experienced restlessness frequently for longer than six months, it might be a sign of GAD.

- Many people with GAD complain about having difficulty concentrating. However, difficulty concentrating is also related to other medical conditions such as depression, so it is not enough evidence to diagnose GAD.
- You always want to put things off because you feel overwhelmed.
- You tend to avoid several situations because they make you anxious.

Physical

- Having tense muscles on most days is another report that doctors look for during diagnosis because it's a common symptom associated with GAD. It is possible that GAD leads to increased muscle tenseness, but it is also possible that muscle tenseness leads to increased GAD, or that a third factor causes both.
- Difficulty falling/staying asleep is strongly associated with anxiety disorders. Many people with GAD report that they wake up in the middle of the night and have difficulty falling asleep. Some research shows that having insomnia during childhood is linked to developing GAD later in life. Insomnia and anxiety are strongly linked but it is

unclear whether anxiety contributes to insomnia, if insomnia contributes to anxiety, or both. However, it has been observed that when a general anxiety disorder is treated, insomnia often improves as well.

- Most people with GAD feel excessive restlessness or irritability.

According to a recent study on over 6,000 adults, it was observed that more than 90% of those with GAD reported feeling irritable, especially when their anxiety level was at its peak.

Young and middle-aged adults with GAD reported twice as much irritability in their daily routine.

- Stomach problems, diarrhea, or nausea are some red flag symptoms associated with GAD.

GAD symptoms in children

Excessive worrying in children centers on past behaviors, future events, family matters, social acceptance, personal abilities, and school performance. Unlike adults with this anxiety disorder, children and teens often don't realize that their anxiety is disproportionate to the event or situation, so adults need to recognize their symptoms. In addition to the many symptoms that appear in adults discussed above, some red flags for GAD in children are:

- "What if" fears; a child with GAD may become so worried about situations far in the future, most of which are beyond their control.
- Perfectionism; you may begin to notice the fear of making mistakes and excessive self-criticism in the behavior of your child.
- Many children with GAD feel that they are to blame for any disaster that may occur, and their worry will keep tragedy from occurring.
- The strong belief that misfortune is contagious and will happen to them in the future. This conviction leads to an anxiety disorder.
- Children with GAD need frequent reassurance and approval because they feel less confident in their abilities and capabilities.

SOCIAL COPING STRATEGIES

When we have GAD, it is common to want to disconnect from others and isolate ourselves. This feeling of loneliness even increases our anxiety. For some people, social strategies can help to manage symptoms and is a vital means to overcome GAD. For instance, going out to watch your favorite games will keep your mind focused on the fun of the game, therefore, keeping every form of anxiety at bay. Below are some social coping strategies to manage your anxiety.

Participating in social activities can make you feel less alone and can also provide a distraction that makes you forget the cause of your impending anxiety.

It is very important that you find someone you can always talk to because talking to someone about your anxiety can make you feel less alone. This is particularly helpful when your worries start spiraling. You could also talk to a specialist on anxiety control.

When you are struggling with anxiety, social activities help you to find a support system. Support groups can provide you with a network of people going through the same thing. There are a variety of support groups available, both online and in-person options, that can be of great significance when it comes to managing GAD.

Anxiety tends to rob us of pleasure and hinders us from having the fun we deserve. Laughter can help alleviate symptoms, and this can be found through friends and family. You can also find humor on television, in books, or online sources.

Know who to avoid when your anxiety is high. Other people

who worry may not be helpful at this time; also, people you know tend to stress you out.

Be aware that your anxiety may get in the way of your relationships at times, leaving you feeling needy and insecure.

Look for anxiety-driven relationship patterns and take steps to reduce them. It is possible that each time you are with someone undesirable, your anxiety level keeps increasing. It is advisable you figure what relationships are and how you can put an end to them.

STRATEGIES TO HELP YOU CALM DOWN QUICKLY

Social Interaction.

Social interaction can help you calm down quickly, but when this isn't possible, you can self-soothe using physical senses:

- Sight: look at things that relax you or make you smile. If you can't go out for a recreational view of tourism centers, you could entertain your sight with family pictures, pets' pictures from the internet, or television.
- Sound: listen to soothing sounds or music or create music with musical Instruments. You could sing your favorite tune or listen to the sounds of nature

(either live or recorded), the wind through the trees, ocean waves, or birds singing.

- Smell: you can also manage your anxiety by lighting scented candles, spraying on your favorite perfume, and breathing in fresh air.
- Taste: having a good taste of your favorite treat will help reduce your anxiety. You could also use a sip of herbal tea as it will also help.
- Touch: self-massage, stroke a pet, stroke a soft blanket, or sitting outside in the cool breeze are very good ways to help you manage GAD.
- Movement: walking around with a friend or pet, jumping up and down and stretching your joints, and dancing are very good ways to manage anxiety.

Reframing Your Worries

The major symptom of GAD is excessive worrying, which is derived from your internal beliefs. You may feel your worries come from external factors, but worrying is self-generated. The trigger is external, but it is your internal dialogue that feeds it.

You probably try to solve problems that haven't happened yet and predict worst-case scenarios. This may feel like self-protection, but it's causing the problem. To save yourself from the psychological stress of anxiety, you have to stop assuming the worst in every upcoming event. You have to develop a sense of optimism. Visualize the event coming to pass in the best possible manner. Don't forget that you may be worrying yourself for an event that may finally happen in your favor.

Try to stop focusing on "what if"s." You probably have a lot of "what if's" running through your head. This increases your heartbeat and anxiety level. To avoid making your GAD worse, you have to stop visualizing upcoming events, especially those that make you uncomfortable. Those worst-case events you have imagined have less than10% chance of actually happening. Is that worth the stress? Hell no. You are obviously paying in advance for a commodity you may likely not get delivered.

Some people with GAD actually think worrying will help them salvage the effects of the unlikely event they have visualized. Let go of the idea that worrying helps you because it doesn't. As a matter of fact, worrying causes more harm to your health.

Challenge Worrisome Thoughts:

Create a daily worry period: To have absolute control over your worries, you have to set time and place for worrying, for instance, in the bathroom from 6:00 to 6:20 pm. You have to ensure your preferred worry period comes way before your bedtime. During this period, you are free to worry about whatever is in your mind.

Distinguish between solvable and unsolvable worries: Problem-solving has to do with evaluating a situation and figuring out concrete steps to remedy the situation. Taking your time to think about the worst-case scenario is never the solution to any upcoming situation. Instead, you need to figure out if your worry is solvable or not. If your worry is actually solvable, you need to spend more time brainstorming on the possible remedies. But if your worry is not solvable, you have to accept the uncertainty.

Interrupt the worry cycle: The thoughts associated with GAD usually come like a boomerang. You have to interrupt the worry circle to give yourself a time out of the excessive and relentless worrying. To do this, you have to engage in one or more of the following:

1. Get up and get moving by engaging in some exercises. They release endorphins that boost energy, relieve stress, and enhance your sense of welfare.

2. Take a tai chi or yoga class. Basically, this has to do with focusing your mind on your breathing and movements.

3. Meditate. This helps in switching your focus from

the past or future to what's happening in the present.

4. Try deep breathing. Worrying increases the rate of your breathing, which increases your anxiety. To take control of your breath and quiet negative thoughts associated with anxiety, you have to practice deep breathing.

Practice Mindfulness

Anxiety is basically worrying about what might take place in the future and what you will do about it. Sometimes it has to do with past events, rehashing the things you have done or said. Mindfulness helps you reduce your worries by conveying your attention to the present each time you get overwhelmed by your worries. With mindfulness, you can figure out where your thinking is doing you damage, and get in touch with your emotions. You have to acknowledge and observe your worries, and not try to fight, ignore, or control them. After figuring out and accepting your worries, you have to let them go. Try as much as you can to always stay focused in the present by paying attention to how your body feels, your ever-changing emotions, the rhythm of your breathing, and the thoughts that drift through your mind. We will discuss more about mindfulness in chapter eight.

· · ·

Practice Relaxation Techniques

The meditation techniques can provide some immediate respite from anxiety and worry. These relaxation techniques will also change your brain if practiced regularly. It will be further discussed in chapter nine.

Learn Your Triggers

In as much as you seek to manage your anxiety, it is also important you pay attention to the things, events, or situations that seem to trigger your anxiety. It may not be easy to avoid those triggers completely, but knowing them will go a long way to helping you gain clarity and enable you to take steps to manage stress in those specific situations.

Practice Acceptance

You don't have to feel bad if you are experiencing anxiety. It is not something you are facing because you are flawed in any way. It is influenced by a number of factors. GAD is something that many people experience, and there is no one cause for it.

Adopt A Positive Attitude

It is important you keep a positive attitude when experiencing GAD. You don't have to lose hope for better living because of GAD. Many people challenged by anxiety live full, joyful, and productive lives. I will recommend some inspiration through verses, quotes, nature, music, and social connections, etc.

Generally, GAD can be a disturbing condition to have, but it is not a death sentence. If you can discipline yourself to follow the tips we have discussed and will still discuss, you will cope with your symptoms and live your best life.

5

LIVING WITH SOCIAL ANXIETY DISORDER

When people give speeches, they experience anxiety. Even the most celebrated orators get this anxiety. The difference between good speakers and people who fumble is that the good speakers know how to conceal their anxiety and proceed with the task as if they are not anxious. If you are one of these bold speakers who don't experience anxiety when you speak, it could be that you get your social anxiety when you are attending an interview. We all do, but to different degrees.

It is not just during speeches or interviews that people get anxious. Many people experience some degree of anxiety in social situations such as parties, schools, dates, and other human-to-human interactions. When moderate, it can be considered normal. But when this anxiety becomes intense and interferes with your life, you may be experiencing social anxiety disorder (SAD), which comes with emotional, behavioral, and physical symptoms and can be very distressing.

As I said in the preliminary chapters of this book, SAD is one of the main types of anxiety disorders. And in this chapter, we will take an in-depth look at this disorder. We will look at the signs and symptoms, thinking styles that fuel it, and self-help, among other things.

WHAT IS SAD?

We know how people can be shy or develop occasional nerves when they are in public, but SAD is more than regular shyness. It is a condition whereby an individual develops an intense fear for certain social situations. The fear can be more intense when the individual is confronting a social situation that they are not familiar with. The fear stems from the erroneous belief that the individual is being watched and evaluated by others. That, most times, is not the case because most times, people are too busy living their own lives that they won't have the spare time to start assessing you.

There is a difference between social anxiety and social anxiety disorder. You need to know the underlying difference. You can get anxious during a social setting. If it starts and ends with that social setting and doesn't linger or try to interfere with your life decisions after that situation, it is just social anxiety. But if you get the anxiety and, because of it, you decide you are never going to be in that setting or anything similar, it is becoming a disorder. If you also catch yourself getting anxious just by thinking of that social setting, then it is a disorder. In a nutshell, you may experience social anxiety in some situations without having SAD. But when your anxiety affects your life and causes great stress, it may be SAD.

People with SAD do not just stop at believing they are being evaluated; they also believe that people's evaluation of them will be negative. Since they are scared that they might be scrutinized, judged or, maybe even embarrassed, they may go to great lengths to avoid these situations. They will do everything to avoid that situation because they don't want to be embarrassed. And even when they just think about those social situations, they may become anxious.

The problem with such avoidance is that you land out avoiding things that are fun and exhilarating for others, such as parties with friends, hangouts, graduation ceremonies, and so on. Apart from that, it can keep you from reaching great heights in your chosen career. That is because you will do everything to avoid assessments such as interviews and examinations. And even when you force yourself to attend because you badly need to do so, you might end up ruining everything because your panic will get the better part of you. Even if you are already working, you try to avoid those presentations and interactions that can grant you promotions and growth in your workplace.

SAD also reduces your confidence and can give you chronic low self-esteem that will force you not to try anything because you have convinced yourself that you are not good enough. In extreme cases, it can spiral into depression, and if not attended to, can lead to isolation, or worst-case scenario, suicide.

So you can see that this is not a disorder you want to live with. If you hadn't realized that you are living with SAD all this while, that is pardonable. Now that you know, you must do everything you can to emancipate yourself from such mental slavery.

If this describes you, all hope is not lost. There are a few proven tips that you can start using today to reclaim your confidence and mingle with people healthily.

CAUSES AND COMMON

If you have SAD, you are not alone; countless other people are with you. Anxiety and Depression Association of America (ADAA) states that, in the U.S., around 40 million people experience one form of anxiety every year, and out of that number, 15 million of them experience social anxiety. SAD is quite common, but different things can cause it in different people.

Common triggers include:

- Meeting new people: If you have SAD, then you know how difficult it is for you to strike up a conversation with a total stranger. That is because you feel that you do not deserve their time, and they shouldn't be talking to you. This is the same reason why you might find it difficult to go on a date. For people with SAD, being on a date or thinking about one can trigger anxiety.

- Small talk: For people with SAD, small talk is not just a mutual communication between pairs; they see it as an evaluation exercise. They start picking their words and being careful. This can lead to a slight mistake in speech, and when that happens, they spiral out of control, and anxiety sets in.

- Public speaking: Even people who do not have anxiety disorders get anxious when speaking in public, and they know it is normal. It doesn't stop them from speaking in public because they understand it is normal. In contrast, people with SAD experience anxiety once, and decide they will never do it again because of how they felt about it the first time. They make it all about themselves and assume that their listeners are there to evaluate them when, in reality, they are there to hear or even learn from them.

Other triggers include:

- Stage performance
- Being the center of attention
- Being watched
- Being teased
- Going on a date
- Talking to authority figures
- Speaking in a meeting
- Using public bathrooms
- Taking exams
- Making phone calls
- Going to parties

Basically, any situation that can make you believe that you are being evaluated can make you anxious if you live with SAD. By that, you will start seeing that situation as a psychologically stressful situation, and you will do anything you can to avoid it. As you start avoiding it, it begins to disrupt your life, and that is when it goes from an annoying situation to a disorder.

SYMPTOMS OF SAD

Symptoms are the subtle or extreme signs that you can use to tell for sure that you are grappling with SAD. Most people live in denial; they like to tell themselves that it is probably normal because they know that every one of us gets anxious.

Being anxious is okay, just as we saw in the first chapter of this book, but when it goes beyond mere anxiety, and you start noticing the following symptoms, you may have SAD.

The symptoms can be divided into emotional, behavioral, and physical.

1. Emotional symptoms: These are the feelings you will get because of the anxiety you feel.

- Excessive self-consciousness.
- Intense worry leading up to a social situation (sometimes months in advance)
- Extreme fear of being judged
- Fear that you'll embarrass yourself
- Fear that others will notice your anxiety

2. Behavioral symptoms: These are some of the behaviors you would put up that you probably wouldn't have if you weren't concerned about people's evaluation of you.

- Avoiding social situations
- Staying quiet and trying to go unnoticed
- Need to bring someone with you
- Drinking before social situations

3. Physical symptoms: These are the ways your physical body will react to the anxiety you are feeling on the inside.

- Blushing
- Shortness of breath
- Stomach upset
- Trembling/shaking
- Racing heart
- Sweating
- Feeling faint

STRATEGIES FOR OVERCOMING SAD

There are several strategies you can adopt to help you deal with this, although they all involve you facing social situations head-on. Just because it involves facing the situation headlong, most people with SAD will prefer not even to try, but that is not you. Just the fact that you are reading this book shows you want to be free. You have to follow this through to reach that freedom.

For you, it will get as easy as it can get because, in this chapter, you will see how misplaced those fears are. When you have learned to see your fears as lacking basis, you will find it easier to face the situations on your way to recovery.

Avoid Negative Coping Strategies

Most people, when they discover that they feel overly anxious about certain social settings, get creative and start looking for things that can help them cope with those settings, especially when it is inevitable. ADAA's statistics that state that 20% of people with SAD also have alcohol use disorder proves this assertion. That would have been great, but the problem is that most of these coping strategies will only harm you in the long run because you have not faced the problem squarely. The most common coping strategy that people adopt is alcohol and substance consumption. Another problem with this is that it can lead to substance dependence and abuse. For instance, if you start taking alcohol to help you get over your panic so that you can address your coworkers at work, you will never be able to address anyone when you are sober. With time, you may become an alcoholic, and that, on its own, has its own demerits.

Also, when you take too much of these substances, it can even worsen your anxiety and lead to further isolation. Research shows that excessive drinking can circle back and cause heightened anxiety, bad moods, and other symptoms such as disrupted sleep patterns. So avoid negative coping strategies by all means. If you have started using them already, stop. Remember that a healthy lifestyle can help you cope with most of the anxiety disorders, and in the third chapter of this book, we said a healthy lifestyle also entails cutting down on alcohol.

Face Your Fear

Rather than looking to hide behind alcohol or other substances, learn to face these situations with sobriety because you will be sober most of the time. And it is only when you have conquered it with your clear eyes that you have truly conquered it. Not everyone will take substances to mask their anxiety. Instead, they will slip into isolation because they want to avoid engaging in social situations as much as they can.

In this era that we live in, isolation is even easier for them because of the internet, smartphones, and social media. People prefer to attend online events and keep ghost friends because they don't want physical contact. As people hide behind their smartphones and become addicted to technology, they begin to display potential markers of social anxiety.

Facing your fear is a therapeutic approach that works because it violates your norms and standards to break the self-reinforcing cycle of fear and avoidance. When you expose yourself to social mishaps, those social settings you are scared of, you gradually begin to see how baseless your fears are. You will realize that instead of your listeners judging you and embarrassing you as you anticipated, they may even give you a standing ovation. You will realize that your perceived threats do not lead to the negative consequences you had conjured in your mind. That will force you to reevaluate the perceived threats.

In essence, that social setting that you dread most should dominate your to-do list. If you dread public speaking, look to snatch every opportunity that comes your way to address people. Do this continually, and it becomes easier.

Reframe Your Thoughts

You have seen how most of the negative consequences that you have framed up are mostly false. It is a thing of the mind because you are what you tell yourself. If you tell yourself that you are not good enough for human interaction, you will live your life believing that. But suppose you tell yourself that you are the best version of you. In that case, you will see yourself as worthy of associating with other people without expecting to be evaluated negatively. Hence, you must learn to reframe your thoughts on how you understand the stress you are experiencing.

Learn to focus on an affirming thought that can make it easier to deal with a social situation. For instance, even if attending a party seems like a daunting task, tell yourself, "the party is scary, but I am a funny and interesting person, so I should blend in just fine because I will have talking points with people I encounter."

It is recommended that for the best result, you should counter each of your negative thoughts with at least three positive ones.

Perform An Act Of Kindness

When you do this, it can help counter negative social expectations by forming an association of positivity with the social environment. The act of kindness can also distract you from focusing on yourself too much, worrying, and conjuring negative thoughts about yourself. Apart from distracting you, kind deeds also have a way of lifting moods and making you happier. Countless research agrees so.

For these reasons, selfless acts of kindness can help people with SAD to feel better in social situations, and one study published in Motivation and Emotion in 2015 agrees.

. . .

Challenge Negative Thoughts

Before you can reframe your thoughts, you have to eliminate the negative thoughts, and one way you can do that is by challenging them.

- Identify negative thoughts: For instance, you may have told yourself that you are not as good as others. That is a negative thought.
- Analyze and challenge the thought: What are your reasons for saying this? Are you created differently than others? What are your reasons for coming up with such a drastic conclusion?
- Logical evaluation: As you begin to pick sentiments apart and evaluate everything logically, it can help you replace these thoughts with more positive and realistic ones.

Unhealthy Thinking Styles

Unhealthy thinking styles can fuel social anxiety. Look for unhelpful thought styles you may be having such as:

- Mind reading: A situation where you will assume that you know what other people are thinking. When you assume this, you will also assume that they see you in the same negative light that you see yourself.

- Fortune telling: When you try to predict the future and foretelling doom for yourself. Beliefs like "If I stand up to talk, I will embarrass myself." When did you start knowing the future?

- Catastrophizing: Exaggerating things more than what they are. For instance, believing that people will notice that you are anxious, and it will be terrible.

- Personalizing: Making everything all about you and assuming that people see you negatively.

Learn to Focus On Other People Rather Than Yourself

It is when you overthink yourself and about people's evaluation of you that anxiety kicks in. Focusing on yourself and how you're feeling in the situation triggers more anxiety and prevents you from being present in the social situation. Learn to shift your attention to others. The more you concentrate on what's happening around you, the less you'll be affected by anxiety.

As you focus on other people, don't try to imagine what they are thinking about you, remember that is what we are trying to avoid.

Here are a few tips to further help you overcome your SAD.

- Remember that your anxiety isn't that visible, so people will be concerned with their affairs rather than judging you.
- Keep your focus on the social setting and listen to what's being said.
- Focus on the present.
- Stop pressuring yourself to be perfect. We are all humans, and we are not perfect. Rather than worrying about your imperfection, channel that energy into improving that aspect of your life if it is possible. But if you can't improve on it, accept it as a part of you and learn to live with it,
- Control your breathing in a social situation. We will be discussing more on controlled breathing when we start discussing more detailed self-care methods for anxiety disorders.
- Make an effort to be more social. SAD wants you to be in isolation, but you know you must not yield to it. So strive to be more social against all the odds.
- Look for supportive social environments that are not focused on socializing, such as classes and voluntary work.
- Practice assertiveness.
- Work on non-verbal communication skills. These

are skills that can make you more confident in social interactions. It involves knowing how to take a relaxed posture because that can encourage people to respond positively to you. Ordinarily, SAD causes you to have a "closed-off" stance that tends to scare people away and reinforce your fear.

- Improve communication skills: When you know how to communicate effectively, you will find it easier to socialize, and you will rarely make those mistakes that can hurt your self-esteem and sink you.

- Be open about your anxiety; talk about it. As you talk about it, you will begin to see how senseless it sounds. Your listener can also help you debunk some of the erroneous beliefs you have about yourself.

Everyday Strategies

- Inform your employer.
- Arrive at meetings/appointments early.
- List questions before an event.
- Keep up with current events to give fodder for small talk.
- Attend events/do a job where you derive true value, so the social elements seem worth it.

- Aim to make new friends.
- Practice healthy lifestyle habits that we discussed in the third chapter of this book.

Above all, remember that social anxiety is not a personality trait, meaning that it does not come naturally as your way of thinking, feeling, and behaving. Therefore, you can work on it.

In conclusion, it can be extremely difficult living with SAD or trying to free yourself from it, but it is possible to set yourself free. You can start by challenging the negative thoughts that trigger your fear and anxiety. Then proceed to face your fears by facing the situations that give you sleepless nights. As you expose yourself to those situations you dread so much, and you realize that they are not as embarrassing as you thought, you will find it easier to face them a second time. It will teach you to stay anxiety-free in those situations you consider stressful. If you practice the self-care approaches we've discussed here, you should do just fine. But if you think you may need extra care and attention, consult a doctor or other mental health professionals.

6

LIVING WITH OBSESSIVE-
COMPULSIVE DISORDER

O CD is yet another common anxiety disorder. Here is a guide to understanding it, its symptoms, triggers, types, diagnosis, risk factors, and some self-care steps that you can adopt today if you have this disorder.

A person might lock the door to their apartment on their way out, and a few meters away from the door, they feel a strong urge to double-check that they locked the door. The person in this context had a genuine reason for double-checking. They simply wanted to be sure their home was secured. They wanted to do it, and they did it. In the case of somebody with OCD, the person in this example will lock the door, know very well that they locked it, yet they will feel a strong compulsion to go and check again. Deep down, they know they locked the door, but the compulsion will get a better part of them. And they will return to check the door even when they know they did. They went back to check the door even when it complicates their life unnecessarily.

WHAT IS OCD?

It is an anxiety disorder characterized by a cycle of obsessions and compulsions, which can be difficult to prevent. If you have OCD, you will normally experience repetitive and unwanted thoughts that lead to excessive urges to do the things that dominate your thoughts. These thoughts are known as obsessions, while excessive urges are known as compulsions. These obsessive thoughts and compulsive behaviors can interfere with your life. When they do, you have OCD.

To better understand OCD, let's look at the obsession and compulsion components individually.

Obsessions: They are thoughts, images, and impulses that recur. They are often disturbing and distracting to you, and they are repetitive.

Compulsions: They are behaviors/rituals that you feel compelled to act out repeatedly, usually as an attempt to reduce obsessions (e.g., fear of contamination = cleaning rituals). But relief does not last, and the obsessions often come back stronger, and the rituals only add to anxiety.

OCD is an anxiety disorder because even when you know that your thoughts and behaviors are illogical, you will still be worried and anxious that if you don't do them, something terrible might happen. Whenever you try to ignore or suppress these thoughts, you will be afraid that the thoughts you are having might just be true. It is when this anxiety becomes too much that you will eventually cave in and engage in those compulsive behaviors. When you engage in the behavior, your anxiety reduces, but only temporarily. Soon, the obsessive thoughts will be on to you again.

With OCD, you are trapped in a cyclical pattern of obsessive thoughts to anxiety to compulsive behavior to temporary relief. When the relief wears off, the obsessive thoughts resume.

While it is possible for some people to experience either obsession or compulsion, others experience obsessions and compulsions together, and that is when it is said that they have OCD.

When you have OCD, obsessive thoughts and compulsive behaviors interfere with your everyday life. It is character-ized by uncontrollable, unwanted thoughts and ritualized behaviors you feel compelled to perform; you may know they're irrational, but you cannot resist them. You may have obsessive thoughts and behave compulsively, and it will not qualify as a disorder. However, whenever these obsessions and compulsions become so distressing that they affect your life, it becomes a disorder.

The brain gets stuck on a thought or urge, which can only be relieved by performing repetitive behaviors.

RISK FACTORS

It has been stated that genetics play a role in OCD. That means that you are more likely to develop it if a biological relative has it.

Most times, OCD doesn't occur alone. It often co-occurs with Attention Deficit Hyperactivity Disorder (ADHD), Tourette's, major depressive disorder, social anxiety disorder, and eating disorders.

The symptoms associated with OCD are often exacerbated by stress.

CATEGORIES OF PEOPLE WITH OCD

People with OCD fall into categories of:

- Washers: these are people who are afraid of contamination. They are characterized by washing compulsions. For instance, you may find yourself washing your hand twenty times before touching a food item because you fear that you may contaminate that food if you don't wash that way.

- Checkers: these people will check something time and time again because they feel that if they don't, they may be exposed to harm or danger. For instance, a checker may visit the kitchen several times, and each time, they check that they turned off the gas cooker because they don't want to burn down the house.

- Doubters and sinners: this category of people have a strong belief that if they fail to do things perfectly, something terrible will happen to them.

- Counters and arrangers: these people's obsessions are with order and symmetry. They are driven by superstitions about numbers, order, colors, and other symmetry-related items. A counter/arranger will spend time checking that a group of items is arranged in a particular manner because they dread something bad will happen if these are not arranged "properly."

- Hoarders: these people are scared that if they dispose of anything, then something bad will happen to them. That will cause them to compulsively keep things even when they don't need it. Hoarders may also suffer from other related mental illnesses such as PTSD, kleptomania,

ADHD, skin picking, depression, compulsive buying, and tic disorders.

SYMPTOMS OF OCD

Symptoms can express themselves through thoughts and behaviors.

Thoughts: The common ones are:

- Fear of contamination
- Fear of harming yourself or others
- Intrusive sexual or violent thoughts
- Excessive focus on religious/moral concepts
- Fear of not having things you may need
- Order and symmetry
- Superstitions

Behaviors: The common behaviors you will notice yourself exhibiting are:

- Excessive checking of objects
- Repeatedly checking on loved ones
- counting/tapping/repeating certain words
- Excessive washing/cleaning
- Ordering and arranging things
- Excessive prayer

- Accumulating junk

COPING STRATEGIES/ SELF-CARE TIPS

Identifying your triggers, practicing exposure and response prevention (ERP), and challenging negative thoughts can help you to manage your condition, as well as making lifestyle changes and adopting techniques that can help with all kinds of anxiety disorders, such as relaxation and meditation techniques.

In the case of OCD, and just about any anxiety disorder that we are discussing so far, I don't need to stress the importance of learning all you can about the condition you have. This is the best way to confront it. Reading this book is a great place to start, but it shouldn't be the last. Learn as much as you can about any of the disorders you have. Without that, your anxiety is higher when you don't have any idea of what is happening to you. Strive to become an expert on your condition, then proceed with the following self-help tips:

Identify your triggers

This is the first step to managing OCD. Your triggers are those thoughts or situations that initiate the obsessions and compulsions. To identify your trigger also means recording it. If something happens and it leads to an obsession, record what happened, and the obsession it led to. Also, record the intensity of the anxiety that ensued and the compulsions that you used to ease the anxiety. For instance, if you are a washer, touching a contaminated substance may trigger an intense fear that you have been contaminated, and you may have to wash your hands for several minutes before you eased the anxiety that followed. In this case, the trigger was the dirty substance. Give the fear or anxiety you felt a number on a scale of one to ten. Then record the number of times you had to wash your hands before the anxiety died down.

Why is this important? When you keep track of triggers, you may be able to anticipate your obsessions. And if you can anticipate them, you will be able to appease them more easily. For instance, if you know that you are a washer, take extra care to wash the first time so that when the urge comes for you to wash again, you know it is a compulsion. Another example is if you are a checker, tempted to check and double-check that you locked the door, pay more attention the first time you locked it.

As you lock the door the first time, create a clear and solid mental picture at the back of your mind that tells you that you locked the door for sure. When you do that, and the urge comes for you to check the door again, you will quickly identify this new wave of urge for what it is: nothing but an obsessive thought.

This routine can help you ease the anxiety that follows. It can also serve as an important tool for you to start learning how to handle other OCD compulsions because as you proceed with one, you will begin to see a pattern that works.

Learn to resist compulsions

You may say, "If I identify my triggers, is it not better to avoid the situations altogether?" That might seem like a good idea, but you have to realize that the more you avoid those triggers, the scarier they get. So instead of avoiding, learn to resist them by exposing yourself to them. Remember how we said in the previous chapter that it was better to expose yourself to the social settings that scare you if you have SAD. Here, too, it is better to expose yourself to your triggers so that, with time, they will no longer be scary.

Exposing yourself to the trigger and learning how to deal with the anxiety without giving in to the urges is how you get over OCD. This technique is called the exposure and response prevention (ERP) technique. Qualified mental health experts use this technique when offering therapy to their patients.

With ERP, you go to where the trigger or source of your obsession is, then you stop yourself from performing the compulsive behavior that would have eased your anxiety. For instance, if you are a washer and you will go to a public restroom, you have to touch the door handle. Normally, this was enough to get you washing and washing again, but this time, keep yourself from washing at all. The anxiety will hit you, but choose to sit this one out. With time, the anxiety will begin to go, and you will realize, much to your amazement, that the anxiety can go away even when you don't give in to your obsession.

It is not going to be the easiest thing you will do, so don't expect an easy ride. The difficulty that comes with it is the reason why you should start with your smallest fears first and move up. Remember that while you were identifying your triggers, you were attaching numbers to them according to their intensity. When you want to start confronting your fears, start with those with a lower intensity number. Arrange your fears in ascending order of intensity and work your way up the ladder.

Challenge obsessive thoughts

We all get troubling thoughts from time to time, and that's normal. But with OCD, your brain is stuck on a particular recurring anxiety-provoking thought. The more distressing the thought is to you, the more you will try to repress it. This attempt to repress it will only cause it to become more bothersome. As with compulsions, you can train yourself with ERP. Remind yourself that your thoughts do not define you; no matter how violent or intrusive they are, they don't make you a bad person. To see your thoughts for what they truly are, do the following:

- Write down your obsessive thoughts. No matter how repetitive it gets, write it down. Doing this will make it lose its power. Also, writing it down is harder than just thinking about them, so it helps your obsessive thoughts to disappear sooner.

- Create an OCD worry period. Schedule specific times to focus on these thoughts. Rather than allowing these thoughts to meddle in your day, set time aside when you can accommodate those worries. I recommend ten minutes each day. During this time, you are focusing on these thoughts but not trying to correct them. After the period, calm yourself and let the thoughts go so you can focus on living your life for the rest of the day. When obsessive thoughts come into your mind, rather than worrying about them, write them down and postpone them to your worry period.

- Challenge the thoughts. Ask yourself, "Is this thought I am having now helpful?" "Are there more positive or realistic views of the situation?" "Is there any evidence that the thought is true, and if there is, what is it?" "If a friend was having this same thought, what would I say to them?"

- Record yourself saying the thought out loud and expose yourself to it regularly to reduce distress.

Find Support

If you have OCD, look to create a support network such as OCD support groups, friends, and family for yourself. This is because OCD can consume you and push you to isolation. And if you give in to isolation, it will only worsen your OCD symptoms, so you must never let it get to that. How can you do that? Through support. Create time for your family and friends. Locate and join OCD groups so you can learn from people's experiences and find support when you will need it.

Manage stress

Try to minimize stress as much as possible because it can trigger symptoms and also aggravate your OCD. You can reduce stress by exercising regularly and spending time with the people who matter in your life. You can also adopt the relaxation techniques we will be discussing later in this book.

Make lifestyle changes:

This has been discussed extensively in chapter three. With

OCD, you need to get enough sleep, eat well, exercise regularly, meditate, and stick with your treatment plan.

- Practice mindfulness: We will discuss more on this in chapter eight.
- Practice relaxation techniques: Refer to chapter nine.
- Become informed about OCD: The more you know about the condition, the better equipped you are to handle it. Also, educating yourself in OCD will expose you to support networks and other people facing similar problems. By reading this book, you have set yourself on the right track. You can still know more about the condition by reading online books and contents on it. You can also talk to your mental wellness experts or doctors if you need any help or information.

In conclusion, treatment of OCD can be done through consultation with a qualified mental health expert who will prescribe medications. Still, these self-help strategies are just as good, if not better, because they help you attack the problem from the roots, and not just improve the symptoms as medication would.

7

THE POWER OF EFT TAPPING IN MANAGING ANXIETY

I know how challenging dealing with anxiety can be. However, on the bright side, there are many effective coping strategies you can use. I have explained the three most common forms of anxiety disorder in the previous sections. By now, you should know that there are some techniques you can use to manage your anxiety, whether it has become a disorder or not. Whether you are aware or not, it is important to know and also identify the type that works for you to help you manage your symptoms while living with the condition.

Exercise, meditation, therapy, and lifestyle changes, among other things, are all wonderful ways that you can use to relieve your symptoms. If you are already practicing any of them, I commend you, because you are already putting in the effort and taking an active role in improving your health and wellbeing.

But again, you may be practicing all these and still suffering from anxiety symptoms. In that case, what should you do?

This is where Tapping comes in. Tapping is a technique that helps in managing anxiety.

WHAT IS EFT TAPPING?

The emotional freedom technique (EFT) was developed by Gary Craig in 1993. It is a form of alternative medicine that is similar to acupuncture. Although Tapping is something that you can do for yourself, you don't need help from someone like you do with acupuncture.

There is ongoing research into EFT. Still, it has been suggested as an effective way to manage anxiety and PTSD. Since it's still undergoing research, it would be best when used with other techniques for managing anxiety.

Simply put, EFT, also referred to as Tapping or psycholog-ical acupuncture, is an alternative treatment for emotional distress.

HOW EFT TAPPING WORKS

The basis of science on Tapping therapy borders on the functions of the amygdala. The amygdala is an almond-shaped part of the human brain. It is part of your limbic system and serves as a source of long-term memory and emotions.

The amygdala is also known as the fear center of the brain. This is where the "flight or fight" response originates. It helps to alert the other part of the brain when it senses danger. In turn, it starts the release of specific hormones and the firing of other brain receptors that make the body respond to a threatened danger.

This is a useful process when you are faced with a real threat and a "need for survival" situation. But it can be injurious when it develops into an illogical fear, i.e., fear of being rejected, or fear of speaking in front of people.

Tapping is effective in turning off the amygdala, inter-rupting the stress response, and giving the brain synapses a chance to rewire for a better emotional response to a situation.

Tapping utilizes the mind-body connection by recognizing and incorporating the concepts that disease, pain, and mental wellbeing are in a complex way connected to your emotional states. Tapping your body can help you create a balance in your energy system.

Your body is fully equipped with an energy system traveling along pathways referred to as meridians. When you tap on the endpoints of these meridians, it helps stimulate the energy system. When the origin of the distress is mentally and verbally addressed, areas with blocked energy will be released and allow a natural flow.

As I have earlier mentioned, Tapping is similar to acupuncture. Healing through acupuncture is achieved through the stimulation of the body's meridian and energy flow, just like how Tapping works. The main difference is that acupuncture makes use of needles, and Tapping doesn't require that. So we can say that one advantage Tapping has against acupuncture is the ditching of needles.

The process of Tapping is a painless and simple one. Anyone can learn it, and you can do it to yourself. Tapping can be used with a particular emotional intention towards your experiences and life challenges. With Tapping, you have access to healing, and you have the power to heal yourself by taking control of your life and destiny.

When Tapping on a basic level, you will need to focus on any negative emotions you are experiencing. This may be an unresolved problem, fear, bad memory, worry, or just anything that bothers you. As you sustain your mental focus on what's at hand, use your fingertips to tap on the specific meridian points of the body, about 5–7 times. There are 12 major meridian points that mirror each side of our body and connect to an internal organ, although the EFT focuses mainly on nine. I will highlight the nine points and where they are located.

- Head (The governing vessel): center, crown, and top of your head. (four fingers)
- Karate chop (The small intestine meridian): below the fingers, the outer hand. (four fingers)
- Under the eye (Stomach Meridian): hard spot under the eye that connects with the cheekbone. (two fingers)
- Eyebrow (Bladder meridian): close to the nose bridge, the inner edges of the eyebrow (two fingers)
- Chin (Central vessel): between the chin and bottom lower lip
- Side of eye (Gallbladder meridian): the hard spot in between the temple and eye. (two fingers)
- Under the arm (Spleen Meridian): four inches below the armpit on your side (four fingers)
- Beginning of collarbone (Kidney Meridian): below the hard ridge of the collarbone (four fingers)

- Under the nose (Governing vessel): the point between the upper lip and bottom of the nose (two fingers)

When you concentrate on negative emotions and tap on these meridian points, your body's energy system and the brain's limbic system engage and thereby encourage a sense of safety. Based on the proof the scientific field of epigenetics gave, there will be external changes (your physical and mental health) when you change your internal environment (beliefs and emotions).

WHAT DOES RESEARCH SAY ABOUT TAPPING?

Just like with most healing art that utilizes ancient wisdom in their practice, Tapping also has its critics. In fact, some psychologists and doctors are quick to dismiss the proof of its healing effect despite ample evidence from case studies, practitioner reports, clinical traits, and testimonies from those who have used Tapping.

Over the years, Tapping has gained popularity, and there has been a growing number of research studies proving that Tapping gives real and lasting healing. Research has suggested that Tapping takes away conditions that medications, hospital treatments, and therapy have failed to resolve.

All around the world, different studies have continued to assert the claim on Tapping, and I have compiled some of them so that you can see for yourself. In this section, we will be looking at some scientific evidence that has supported the healing power of EFT for anxiety and depression.

According to a 2019 study that involved 203 participants, there was a test carried out to see the psychological symptoms and physical reactions of individuals that were attending the EFT workshops. The majority of people in this study were women over the age of 50 (Bach et al., 2019).

After the workshop, the researchers reported that there was a great reduction in the participant's anxiety and depression symptoms, as well as in their cravings and level of pain. There was also an improvement in their level of happiness.

Research has also suggested that physical measures can improve blood pressure, heart rate, and the level of stress hormone. According to a 2016 review of fourteen studies on EFT, people who made use of EFT experienced a great reduction in anxiety. The author does recommend that more studies should be carried out to compare standard treatments like cognitive behavioral theory (CBT) with EFT. (Clond, 2016)

Also in 2016, a random and controlled trial carried out a comparison of how effective CBT and EFT is in the treatment of people with anxiety. The study comprised ten people who enrolled in an 8-week program or either EFT or CBT. The results of this trial showed that both CBT and EFT worked as they reduced the symptoms of anxiety.

Another research that involved students with anxiety revealed that EFT was able to help them feel more relaxed and calm.

Not only these studies I have highlighted, but several others have suggested that EFT is effective when treating a condition like anxiety.

Some of these studies are small and limited, and the criticism is that some of the older studies may have flaws in their methods, suggesting that the results are defective and shouldn't be relied on. While more research is needed before definitive conclusions can be drawn on the effectiveness of EFT, the fact remains that it is an option to consider when you want to feel relief.

EFT TAPPING SEQUENCE

As earlier mentioned, Tapping can be used to resolve different health issues. It is important to know how to use it. This brings us to the EFT Tapping sequence, how it works, and how to do it.

So basically, this is how a basic Tapping sequence works:

Identify the problem.

First, for this technique to be effective, you need to identify the problem you want to focus on. What is your fear? This can be general anxiety or a particular issue or situation that makes you feel anxious. This will be your main point as you start Tapping. Focus on that particular fear—this will help to enhance your result.

Take into consideration the situation or problem.

After identifying the problem, the next thing to do is to consider the situation. How exactly do you feel? Then set a yardstick for the level of the situation's intensity. Using a scale of 0 to 10, rate the intensity level of your anxiety. The 10 represents the highest level, while the zero represents the lowest level. Establishing the yardstick will help you observe your progress after you complete an EFT sequence. At the end of the sequence, if your intensity level was 5 compared to the 10 that you started with, then you have recorded a 50% improvement level.

Create a setup declaration.

Before Tapping, you need to have a phrase or statement that describes what you are addressing. The declaration comes with two goals—to acknowledge the issues you are trying to deal with, and a clear assertion of yourself irrespective of the issue.

Your setup statements can be:

- *"Although I am feeling this anxiety, I still accept myself passionately and totally."*
- *"Although I am having trouble breathing, I still accept myself passionately and totally."*
- *"Although I am feeling anxious about my upcoming interview, I still accept myself passionately and totally."*
- *"Although I am feeling anxious about being broke and trapped in a financial situation, I still accept myself passionately and totally."*
- *"Although I am still panicking about how things will turn out, I still accept myself passionately and totally."*
- *"Although I am worried about how I am going to approach my boss and ask for a raise, I still accept myself passionately and totally."*

The setup statements are not limited to the above; you can alter the examples so that they can fit your situation. Whichever you use, just make sure it addresses your problem and not that of someone else. For example, it is wrong to say,

"Although my friend is troubled, I still accept myself passionately and totally."

Now you can start Tapping!

- With your four fingers on one of your hands, start Tapping the Karate Chop (KC) point of your other hand. Remember that the Karate Chop Point is the opposite side of the thumb, the outer part of the hand (edge).
- Now, put your setup declaration to use by repeating it aloud three times, as you simultaneously tap the Karate Chop point.
- Take a deep breath.
- Next, tap each of the remaining eight meridian points in the sequence. I will be listing them below. Tap each of the points for about 5–7 times.

Eyebrow Point (EB)
Side of Eye (SE)
Under Eye (UE)
Under Nose (UN)
Chin Point (CP)
Collarbone Point (CB)
Under Arm (UA)
Top of Head (TH)

- As you are Tapping on the meridian points, repeat a reminder phrase. For instance, "my brokenness" or "my worry" or "my anxiety" or "my anxiety." The reminder phrase will mentally help you focus on the problem.
- Pause and take another deep breath.
- You have now completed this sequence.
- After completing the sequence, you need to focus on the issue again. When compared to a few minutes ago, is your anxiety level intense? Use a scale of 0 to 10 to give it a rating. Is there a shift in the rating? If the level of your anxiety is higher than 3, then you need to take another round of Tapping. You need to keep Tapping through the sequence until you notice that your symptom is gone or, at least, greatly reduced.

In the next sequence, you can slightly change your setup declarations to take a record of the fact that you are putting in an effort to fix the issue or your zeal to see progress. For instance, you can slightly change it to:

- "Although I still have some anxiety, I accept myself passionately and totally."
- "Although I am still facing financial challenges, I accept myself passionately and totally."

- "Although I am still worried about how to approach my boss for a raise, I still accept myself passionately and totally." And the list goes on and on.

What you have just done is focus on dismissing your current anxiety. Now you can work on bringing some positive energy to take the place of the anxiety. The approach you are using is unlike the traditional "positive thinking." With this approach, you are not trying to hide the anxiety and stress you are feeling with a façade of untrue affirmations or trying to be dishonest with yourself. What you are doing is dealing and confronting the anxiety, together with the related negative emotions, and offering yourself a passionate and total acceptance to yourself and your feelings.

After clearing up your emotional dirt, you can now turn your vibrations and thoughts to the positive.

Tapping isn't just a mental trick; it is so much more. And this is why it is more effective than the other positive thinking techniques you may have tried. By Tapping, you are changing your body's energy and biochemistry to a more positive course.

Here are some positive phrases you can make use of:

- *"I am hopeful in my ability to change."*
- *"I am in love with the person I am."*

- *"I am happy with the positive changes I see."*
- *"I am becoming a more cheerful and relaxed person."*
- *"I am achieving a lot."*
- *"I am enjoying the peace and calmness I have."*

The positive phrases above can be used with the same sequence of the Tapping points I have given you.

Now that you know how to Tap, let me give you some tips to guide you through the Tapping sequence and make sure you are using the technique correctly. What's the use of all that you have read in this section if Tapping isn't done in the right way?

So, below are the tips:

- When Tapping, use firm but moderate pressure. It should be the same as testing a melon to see if it is ripe or using your hands to drum on top of a table.
- When Tapping, make use of all four of your fingers, or the first two fingers—the index finger and the middle finger. The two fingers are mostly used for sensitive areas like around your eyes, while the four fingers are used in wide areas.
- Don't use your fingernails to Tap; use your fingertips.

- You can Tap both sides of your body or just one side. The eight meridian points are balanced on either side of your body.

Conclusively, EFT Tapping has so far proven to be an alternative treatment for some physical and health conditions. At the very least, Tapping will help you focus your attention on important things and reduce your disturbing thoughts. As mentioned earlier, research supports it and has indicated that it is an effective treatment for anxiety. Although many people have found EFT helpful, it isn't advisable to rely upon it in isolation. If you are considering using EFT, you should speak to your doctor first.

While it is possible that self-treatment with Tapping can make some people feel better and reduce their symptoms, it is also important that you seek professional help when you experience emotional and physical issues.

In the next chapter, we'll be looking at another great technique that is effective in treating anxiety. This technique is also easy to do and does not require help from someone else. Stay with me as we explore mindfulness and how to do it in the next chapter.

8

MINDFULNESS: HOW TO DO IT AND HOW IT CAN HELP YOU

Mindfulness is the ability to be fully conscious of the present and aware of what you are doing and where you are, and not overwhelmed or reactive by what's going on around you. We are naturally mindful as humans; all we have to do is practice it daily, and it will become habitual.

Each time you bring awareness to your state of mind through your emotions and thoughts, or to what you're directly experiencing through your senses, you're mindful. Current research shows that when you groom your brain to be mindful, you're reshaping your brain's physical structure to help reduce anxiety.

Each time you practice meditation, you venture into the workings of your mind: your sensations (the cool breeze blowing on your skin), your emotions (hate that, love this, loathe that, crave this) and even your thoughts (you may imagine how weird it would be to see an elephant playing the trumpet).

Practicing mindfulness aids you to focus your attention on the present. It draws your focus away from worries about the past or the future. Thus, it is a great tool for managing anxiety. It has several physical and psychological benefits and can be practiced easily at home. Try to practice 3–4 times a week to incorporate mindfulness into your life and help you to manage anxiety symptoms.

It enables you to suspend judgment and unleash your curiosity about your mind's activities and approach your experience with kindness and warmth toward yourself and others.

It helps to teach us how to respond to stress with awareness rather than acting on instinct.

It encourages us to accept our emotions, making it easy to identify and process them, and it enables you to see things from different points of view.

SEVERAL BENEFITS:

Many medical practitioners have done in-depth investigations on the benefits of mindfulness. The overall evidence shows that meditation helps improve various conditions such as anxiety, stress, depression, pain, high blood pressure, and insomnia. Preliminary research also shows that meditation helps people with fibromyalgia and asthma. Meditation also has been shown to improve attention, sleep, and diabetes control, and decrease job burnout. In summary, meditation helps you experience emotions and thoughts with greater acceptance and balance.

Mindfulness improves wellbeing.

Improving the level of mindfulness supports many attitudes that lead to a more satisfying life. Mindfulness makes it easier to manage the pleasures in life as they occur, helps you become fully engaged in activities, and improves your ability to deal with stressful events. Being mindful reduces your chances of getting caught up in worries about regrets over the past, or a future event you think may go wrong. A mindful person is less preoccupied with concerns about self-esteem and success, and can easily form deep connections with others.

. . .

Mindfulness improves physical health.

Apart from giving you greater wellbeing, scientists have discovered that mindfulness helps improve our physical health in several ways. Mindfulness techniques can treat heart disease, help relieve stress, lower blood pressure, improve sleep, reduce chronic pain, and alleviate gastrointestinal difficulties.

Mindfulness improves mental health.

In recent investigations by psychotherapists, mindfulness meditation is great for treating several problems such as anxiety disorders, depression, eating disorders, substance abuse, and couple's conflict.

Body awareness.

This has to do with noticing sensations in the body. Current findings by those who have used mindfulness techniques show that it increases perceptions of body awareness.

Focused attention.

Mindfulness increases the ability to focus attention. Neuroimaging studies show that mindfulness improves the activation of the brain area known as the anterior cingulate cortex (ACC). This area is involved in attention and executive function, and enables us to focus attention on the present rather than being distracted by worry.

Self-perception.

Research found that two months of mindfulness practice changes self-perspective and increases self-esteem and self-acceptance.

Physical health.

Besides reducing anxiety, mindfulness has other health benefits such as reduced cortisol levels and blood pressure.

MINDFULNESS TECHNIQUES

Mindfulness can be practiced in several ways, but each mindfulness technique aims to achieve total control over feelings and emotions by engaging in focused relaxation and deliberately paying attention to sensations and thoughts without judgment. This practice allows the mind to refocus on the present. All mindfulness techniques are a form of meditation.

Basic mindfulness meditation: This has to do with sitting quietly and focusing on breathing or on a word (mantra) that you repeat silently. Let your thoughts flow without any judgment, and ensure you return your focus to your mantra or breath.

Body sensations: In this mindfulness technique, when you notice subtle sensations in the body such as tingling or itching, let them pass without judgment. You have to notice each part of your body in sequence from head to toe.

Sensory: Notice sounds, sights, smells, touches, and tastes. You have to name them accordingly "sound," "sight," "smell," "touch," or "taste," without judgment and let them pass.

Emotions: You have to permit emotions to be present without judgment. You need to practice a relaxed and steady naming of emotions: "anger," "frustration," "joy." Accept the presence of each emotion without judgment and let them pass.

Urge surfing: With this mindfulness technique, you have to cope with cravings (for addictive behaviors or substances) and let them pass. Also, you have to notice how your body feels when the craving comes. Finally, you have to replace the wish for the craving with the knowledge that it will subside.

All these techniques build concentration practices by following the same key principles:

Go with the flow.

To begin mindfulness meditation, you have to establish

concentration by observing the flow of inner emotions, thoughts, and bodily sensations without judging them as bad or good.

Pay attention.

The external sensations such as sounds, sights, and touch that you notice during meditation make up your moment-to-moment experience. The problem is not to latch onto a particular sensation, idea, emotion, or to get caught in thinking about the future or past. Instead, you have to watch what comes and goes in your mind and realize the mental habits that give you a feeling of suffering or wellbeing.

Stay with it.

From the onset, this process may not seem relaxing at all, but over time it gives you greater self-awareness and happiness as you become comfortable with a wider and wider range of your experiences.

MINDFULNESS TRICKS TO MANAGE ANXIETY

Apply these mindfulness tricks to ease anxiety and ease your mind.

Create a worry diary: It is difficult to rationally analyze worrisome thoughts as they swirl and dance through your innocent mind. By writing them on a paper, they will be easier to tackle using a structured set of questions. When this is done accurately with a worry diary, you can find the truth, which will help you stop worrying about what is likely to occur.

Step 1: Write down your worries: When your worries start interfering with daily activities or when you start feeling overwhelmed, take some minutes to write down exactly what you are worrying about.

Why you need to write down your worries:

1. Writing them down eliminates some of their effect over you. You no longer have to meditate over them once you have them in your notebook.
2. Discharging your worries to the notebook frees up some headspace and helps you think clearly.
3. Once you have all your worries written down, you can commence a structured worry-challenging exercise.

Step 2: Clarify Your Worries: After writing down all your worries, you need to clarify and identify them in writing. Afterward, you can start evaluating and challenging these distressing thoughts.

To clarify your worries, you need to ask yourself the following questions.

- What bad thing do I think is going to take place?
- What is the chance that this bad thing is going to happen?
- What are my emotions at the moment?
- What's the force of these emotions?

For instance:

- I am worried the transaction into my account won't be completed.
- I think something is wrong with the transaction. I have not gotten any updates from the bank.
- I am feeling anxious right now.
- 75 out of 100

Step 3: Challenge anxious thoughts: In this step, you have to examine how valid your worries are, through challenging questions aimed to elicit truth and reality.

To challenge your worries, ask, and answer the following questions.

- What evidence supports my worry?
- Is there any evidence against my worry?

- In reality, what is the probability that what I am worried about is actually going to happen?
- What's the worst-case scenario?
- What's the best-case scenario?
- What will probably happen?
- Is being fearful about it helping at all?
- Can I cope if my worst-case scenario happens?
- What can I do to remedy the situation?
- Can I see this situation from another dimension?

Step 4: Reframe the situation: After successfully asking and answering the challenge questions, you have to finalize the processing of this worry.

Set an intention: Irrespective of when you do it, setting an intention helps you focus and reminds you why you are doing something. That's why most yoga teachers instruct that you set an intention for your practice each day. If something gives you anxiety—like writing an exam in school—set an intention for it.

For instance, you can set an intention to treat your body with kindness before eating or to care for your body before heading to the gym.

Do a guided mindfulness or meditation practice: There are many apps and online programs available to enable you to practice a guided meditation without committing to an expensive class or taking up much time.

Doodle or color: Dedicate a couple of minutes to doodle. Invest in a coloring book. This will help eliminate the thoughts that bring you anxiety as your mind gets focused on the coloring book.

Go for a walk: Being outside is a great way to reduce anxiety. Go for a walk, pay attention to the feel of the wind against your skin, the sounds around you, and the smells around you. Ensure your phone doesn't distract you (keep it in your pocket or better yet, at home), and try to stay in the moment by focusing on your environment and your senses.

Wish other people happiness: A few seconds is enough for you to execute this wonderful trick from the author and former Google pioneer Chade-Meng Tan. You have to randomly wish for someone to be happy throughout the day. This practice is all in your head. Try it on your commute, at the gym, at the office, or while you wait in line. If you find yourself annoyed with someone, you have to stop and (mentally) wish them happiness instead.

Look up: Whether you are coming home late or taking out the trash, pause and take a few deep breaths into your stomach as you look up at the stars. With eyes up, let the cosmos remind you that life is bigger than the situation.

Focus on one thing at a time: Your to-do list can be a form of mindfulness if you develop it well and keep to it. Set a timer for five minutes or less and dedicate your full and undivided attention. Don't check your phone, no browsing online, no clicking on notifications. In fact, absolutely no multitasking. Focus on that one task at hand until the timer goes off.

Leave your phone behind: The fact is, you really don't have to take your phone along when going to the next room, when you sit down to eat, or when you go to the bathroom. Keep your phone in the other room, and it will still be there when you are done. Don't worry about it. Sit and breathe before you start eating. You need to create a moment for yourself and your needs in the bathroom or any other place you need to be.

Turn household tasks into a mental break: Relax into the moment instead of obsessing yourself over your to-do list or clutter. Focus on the way the soap flows down the tiles while you clean the bathroom or dance while you do the dishes. Daydream while you fold the laundry. Take a series of slow breaths while you wait for the microwave to stop.

. . .

Journal: There is no best or worst way to journal. You can start with a structured five-minute journal, or you could opt for scribbling your thoughts on a random piece of paper. The act of writing can help console the mind and quiet swirling thoughts. Jot down three amazing things that happened today.

Pause at stoplights: Don't time travel or wish to make cars move out of your way when you're running late. Instead, bring your focus inward at every stoplight. While you wait for the stoplights, sit still and upright and take five slow, deep breaths. This exercise may sound easy and meaningless on a leisurely drive, but the benefits will help you when your stress and anxiety level is high.

Log out of all of your social media accounts: It's true that social media has its uses, but it can also interrupt your productivity and contribute to your anxiety. You'll be amazed at how often you check your accounts without thinking. So, log out.

When you actually want to check-in, set an intention, or better still, a time limit. That way, you won't end up feeling guilty for spending 20 minutes looking at a stranger's pet or getting behind on your work.

You may also, if possible, delete some social media accounts.

A recent study found that using numerous social media platforms increases the level of anxiety in young adults.

Check out: Steadily trying to be mindful at all times can actually add to stress and anxiety. Know when you need to let your mind wander where it wants to go.

Practicing mindfulness meditation 3–4 times a week can help you bring mindfulness into your life and manage your anxiety. The more you do it, the more effective it gets. Mindfulness works well when coupled with relaxation techniques. In the next chapter, we will explore relaxation techniques so you can combine them for the best outcomes.

EFFECTIVE RELAXATION TECHNIQUES FOR ALL TYPES OF ANXIETY

The whole concept of anxiety means you are tensed and riled up. If you can find a means of relaxing your body when you are anxious, and when you are not, you will reduce the anxiety episodes you suffer, and the severity too. To be relaxed, you have to know how to activate your body's relaxation response. If you master it, it can help you to manage your anxiety.

Several techniques are available that you can use to activate your body's relaxation response. Techniques like deep breathing and progressive muscle relaxation can give you tools you can use anywhere to help manage anxiety as it arises. But even when it hasn't occurred, it will be helpful to you if you can build relaxation into your everyday life to ensure that your anxiety is continually being addressed even before they arise.

When we talk about relaxation, we are not saying you should zone out in front of the TV. While that type of relaxation is great, it does not address the effects of stress and anxiety.

The relaxation technique I speak of is capable of activating your body's natural relaxation response—a state of deep rest that slows breathing and heart rate, lowers blood pressure, and rebalances mind and body.

While people often achieve this state through meditation, there are other relaxation techniques you can employ to achieve it. Try different techniques and activities to see what works best for you, your anxiety, and your lifestyle. A technique that works for your neighbor might not work for you. But since there are several techniques to choose from, there will always be something for you.

DEEP BREATHING:

If you have been anxious before, then you know how fast your breathing becomes. This fast breathing is the body's way of trying to provide the brain with all the nutrients and oxygen it needs to cope with the numerous activities going on in there. But often, the body is unable to meet up, and you will start experiencing symptoms such as breathlessness, lightheadedness, dizziness, and tingly feelings in your hands and feet. Since the heart is beating fast, it also increases blood pressure. These symptoms are frightening, so they lead to further anxiety and panic.

But when you reduce the activity in the brain and effectively reduce the pace of your breathing, these symptoms will reduce or disappear totally, and you can calm yourself down. That is what deep breathing does for you.

It simply involves breathing deeply from your diaphragm. This technique is easy to learn and can be practiced anywhere, which means you can use it to help in the face of an anxiety attack. You can also incorporate it into your everyday living even when you are not having an attack.

It stimulates the vagus nerve, activation relaxation response. The vagus nerve extends from the head, through the neck and chest all the way to the colon. As you stimulate it, it activates your relaxation response, and that action lowers stress levels, reduces your heart rate and blood pressure. It is a cornerstone of many other relaxation practices. Most other relaxation techniques will require that you calm yourself first with deep breathing before starting them. Thus, it can be combined with other relaxing things like baths, aromatherapy, and music.

* * *

Steps for Practicing Deep Breathing:

1. Sit or lie in a comfortable position that will allow you to straighten your back. Place one hand on your stomach and the other on your chest.
2. With your hands in place, inhale in such a manner that the hand on your stomach rises while the other hand remains steady or rises just slightly.
3. Breathe out through your mouth and push out all inhaled air. Contract your abdominal muscle, ensuring that only the hand on your stomach moves, while the hand on your chest stays steady.
4. Continue the process, each time ensuring that your stomach lowers and rises as much as it can. Both breathing should be done slowly for the best impact.

If you discover that you can breathe better from your stomach when lying down than when sitting, then always lay down when practicing your deep breathing. With your back on the ground, you can place a small book on your stomach and ensure that the book rises when you breathe in and falls when you breathe out.

The steps above are straightforward enough, but if you are having issues with following it, you can get videos and apps that will guide you through. The procedure is mostly similar.

PROGRESSIVE MUSCLE RELAXATION

Most times, when you are anxious or stressed, your body reacts with muscle tension. This exercise helps you relieve that tension. The idea here is that if you know how to do it even when you are not tense, you can just do it easily and relieve your body of the tension it will be subjected to when you are anxious.

It is a two-step process that involves systematically tensing and relaxing different muscle groups in your body. PMR (Progressive Muscle Relaxation) helps you familiarize yourself with what tension and relaxation feel like in different parts of your body. But you can only gain such intimate familiarity with regular practice. That intimate familiarity will help you promptly detect and react to the first signs of muscular tension. It is this muscular tension that accompanies stress that eventually puts you in a state of tension. So when you cut out the muscular tension, you can relax your body, and your mind will be relaxed as well. That is because as the body relaxes, so does the mind.

Progressive muscle relaxation can give you additional stress relief when you combine it with deep breathing.

Steps for Practicing Progressive Muscle Relaxation

Before you start this exercise, ensure that you do not have any condition that can be aggravated by this exercise, such as muscle spasms, back pains, or any underlying serious injuries. You can consult with your physician if you are not sure.

Seeing how the exercise is all about tensing and relaxing certain muscles, it is advisable you start from your feet and proceed to your face, taking care that no muscle is left out.

Proceed in the following manner:

1. Get comfortable by loosening any tight outfit and being bare-footed.
2. Practice deep breathing for a few minutes, ensuring that you breathe deeply and slowly.
3. When you are ready, start with your right leg. Inhale and tense the muscle group, hold for ten seconds.
4. Breathe out and relax the muscle group suddenly and completely. Take note of the word "suddenly." Don't make the mistake of relaxing it gradually. As you slowly relax the muscle, take note of how tension flows away from your leg and how limp and loose it feels afterward.

5. Let your body relax for 10–20 seconds, then work on your next muscle group, in this case, your left leg. Follow the same sequence of tensing and releasing your muscles described above.

6. From your left leg, work the other relevant muscles as follows:

- For your buttocks, press them together tightly.
- For your stomach, tense by sucking it into a tight knot and releasing it gradually.
- For the chest, inhale deeply and hold for about ten seconds.
- For your hands, clench them for tension and slow-release tension by opening them.
- For your wrists and forearms, extend them and push your hands back at your wrist.
- For your biceps and upper arms, clench your hands first, then bend your arms at your elbow and flex the biceps.
- For your shoulders, shrug them by raising them towards your ears.
- For the back of the neck, press it against the floor or chair.
- For your cheeks and jaws, smile as widely as possible.

- For the muscles around your mouth, tense them by pressing your lips together tightly.
- For your eyes, close them as tightly as possible. Note that this exercise cannot be done while wearing contact lenses. Remove them first, and after the exercise, you can put them back in.
- For your forehead, wrinkle it into a deep frown.

If you are new to progressive muscle relaxation, it might be helpful for you to use video or audio resources so that you will get conversant with the muscle groups and how to transition between them. You can check your local library, or use online video resources for this purpose.

BODY SCAN MEDITATION

The idea here is that when we are stressed, most of the physical discomfort we feel, such as tense muscles, pains, and headaches are mostly connected with our emotional state. Therefore, when you perform the body scan meditation, you are aiming to release the tension that you might not have noticed that you are experiencing.

In this technique, you will focus attention on various parts of your body so you can detect any bodily sensation that you may be having. It is advisable to start with your feet and work up, focusing on how each part of the body feels. As you do this, do not label any feeling as good or bad. Just be aware of them so you can learn from them so you can better manage them.

This relaxation technique breaks the cycle of physical and psychological tension that we often have as humans.

Here is how you can practice it:

1. Start by getting cozy and by getting into a comfortable position where you can easily stretch your limbs.
2. Close your eyes so you can truly focus on your body parts. Start by focusing on your breath, and notice the sensation of how your breath fills and leaves your lungs as you breathe.
3. It is advised you start from your leg, but you can start from any area of your body, just ensure you don't leave out any body part.
4. Any spot you choose to start, focus on that portion as you breathe slowly and deeply. Try to notice any sensation of pain, discomfort, tension, or anything unusual. Don't rush it; ensure you observe the sensation, if any. Slowly release your mental awareness on this body part before proceeding to other parts.
5. As you proceed, do not allow your thoughts to drift

off. Remain in the moment.

When you finish, lie still for a while and notice how your entire body feels. Throughout the exercise, ensure that you give yourself all the time you need to truly investigate and experience every part of your body.

VISUALIZATION

This relaxation technique involves imagining a scene in which you feel peaceful and free. You are to choose any setting that is most calming to you. It may be a movie scene, a favorite childhood spot, a sunny beach, or whatever scene that calms you. Try to let go of all tension and anxiety in the scene. It is also known as guided imagery. You can practice it on your own or with an app, listening aid, or video resource.

You can practice visualization through the following steps:

- Start by getting into a comfortable position in a comfortable and quiet place.
- Close your eyes and imagine your desired place.
- As you picture and imagine the place, be as detailed as possible. You can do that by engaging all your senses which are sight, smell, taste, sound, and feel.

For instance, if your peaceful spot is a tropical beach, try to see the waves, hear birds chirping in the distance and the waves crashing, and feel the water against your feet, and so on.

- Try to enjoy what you are feeling while letting yourself forget all the worries, tension, and anxiety you may be having.

When you feel like you have relieved yourself of every tension, you may gently open your eyes and return back to the present.

SELF-MASSAGE

You must have heard of people going to spas and health clubs to get a massage from professionals at exorbitant prices. That's because it can be massaging yourself or receiving a massage from someone else that reduces stress, relieves pain, and eases muscle tension. If you can get someone to massage you, you should, but if you can't, take a few minutes to self-massage between daily tasks or the end of the day. You can enhance the relaxation you get by combining it with mindfulness, deep breathing, or aromatherapy. You can also use scented lotions and aromatic oil to enhance relaxation.

You can carry out self-massage through the following steps:

1. Knead the muscles of your shoulder and the back of your neck. To do this, make a loose fist with your hands and drum quickly on the back of your neck. Next, massage the base of your skull by making tiny circles there with your fingers. Then tap your scalp with your fingers moving from side to side.

2. Massage your face by making a tiny circle with your fingertips. Take note that you massage your temples, forehead, and jaw muscles properly.

RHYTHMIC MOVEMENTS/MINDFUL EXERCISE

A rhythmic exercise that gets you in a flow of regular movement can produce a relaxation response. Examples of such rhythmic movements are running, swimming, walking, dancing, rowing, and climbing. You can combine this with mindfulness by paying attention to how your body feels in the moment rather than focusing on your anxiety.

If in the process of practicing this technique, your mind wanders to other thoughts, try and refocus yourself by gently returning your thought to the sensations in your body parts.

YOGA/TAI CHI

Tai chi and yoga have physical benefits as well as relaxation benefits for managing anxiety. If you are new to yoga and tai chi, it is best to start with a class because injuries can occur if it is performed wrong. Once you have learned the basics, then you can start practicing alone and modifying it to suit your personality and needs.

Yoga is a sequence of stationary and moving poses, combined with deep breathing to relieve stress and anxiety. It can also be used to improve one's stamina, balance, flexibility, and strength. The types of yoga that focus on slow, steady movement, deep breathing, and gentle stretching are best for anxiety management. Examples are Satyananda, Power and Hatha.

Tai chi is slow, flowing body movements that force you to focus on the movement and your breathing, thereby clearing your mind. It is believed that by focusing on these flows, you can remain in the present, and that is what clears your mind and brings you relaxation.

Tai chi is best learned in a class. If you feel this is a relaxation technique that you want to explore, consider signing up with a fitness class in your neighborhood that offers tai chi classes. As with yoga, once you have learned the basics, you can start practicing alone and tailoring your practice as you desire.

OTHER FORMS OF RELAXATION

Deliberate relaxation can also come in the form of doing activities you enjoy and focusing on those activities (mindfulness) rather than your anxiety. This might include

- Art - drawing/painting/coloring/crafting
- Reading
- Long bath listening to soothing music
- Listening to music

None of the relaxation techniques we've discussed here will yield benefits straightaway. It takes time and practice before you will start reaping any meaningful benefits. Try not to skip days, but even if you do, don't allow it to stop you. Start again and keep going with the goal in your mind.

It is best if you can set up a time in your daily schedule when you will practice any of these relaxation techniques so that when that time is approaching, your body will start entering the mood.

In conclusion, relaxation techniques can be helpful for

relieving moderate anxiety. But when it is extreme, you may need to consult a doctor and get professional treatment. In the next chapter, we will discuss some of the therapy and medication options available to you if these relaxation techniques we've discussed don't work for you.

THERAPY AND MEDICATION: WHAT ARE YOUR OPTIONS?

Most people can manage their anxiety through self-help strategies and lifestyle changes, but sometimes, your symptoms may be so great that you require professional help. If self-help methods aren't working for you, you just might need something a little extra, but be sure you gave self-help strategies a fair chance.

The most used types of therapy for anxiety disorders are cognitive behavioral therapy (CBT) and exposure therapy (ET). If these ones fail, medication can be prescribed, but this varies between patients, and your therapist will devise the right treatment plan for you depending on your type of disorder and the severity.

In this chapter, we will explore the therapy and medication options that are available to you.

I know you badly want to practice the self-help strategies that we discussed in the previous chapter. But if you have tried and your symptoms prove to be too big for them, you have to do the right thing. The general guide is that once your symptoms (worries, fears, or anxiety) are so significant that they have started bringing distress to you and disrupting your daily routine. You have to involve a professional who will either follow you up with therapy or medication. While you are on therapy and medication, you can continue with the self-help strategies as they can still help you manage your anxiety, but don't substitute them for professional help when there is a need for one.

If you are experiencing a lot of physical symptoms, start with a medical checkup. That is because sometimes anxiety can be caused by a medical condition such as asthma, hypoglycemia, and thyroid problems. Therefore, a checkup rules out the possibility that your symptoms are due to one of these medical conditions. Once it has been proven with a checkup that you do not have any medical condition that can manifest itself in the form of the symptoms you are getting, then you may have one of the anxiety disorders.

Once medical problems have been ruled out, consult a therapist who specializes in anxiety disorders. They will conduct some assessments to be sure that what you have is anxiety, and they will tell which of the anxiety disorders you have and the probable cause. Since it is possible for certain medications to cause you anxiety, the mental expert will also go over all your prescriptions to be sure you are not on any risky medications. Prescriptions, such as over-the-counter medications and recreational drugs, will be checked. Then they will devise a treatment plan tailored to your needs.

MEDICATIONS

Medication is sometimes prescribed for anxiety disorders, but it is usually only a temporary measure to relieve symptoms. It is particularly essential when your anxiety is enough to stop you from functioning. However, medications must be prescribed and closely monitored by a mental health expert because anxiety medications can be addictive and cause undesirable side effects.

This is why it should be your last line of defense. You should only use it when every other thing we've discussed fails. You should try changes in lifestyle, therapy, exercise, and the self-help strategies we discussed. Oftentimes, they will be all you need. If, however, they fail, you can consider medication.

Medication for GAD

With GAD, medications are temporary measures to help relieve you of your symptoms at the beginning of your treatment. For long-term treatment, therapy will be mostly used as they have more long-term success than medications.

A medication commonly prescribed for GAD includes:

- Buspirone: It is an anti-anxiety drug that is generally considered as the safest medication for GAD. It only serves to reduce anxiety symptoms and not to eliminate the anxiety. It can be identified by the brand name "Buspar."
- Benzodiazepines: This is another anti-anxiety drug like buspirone, but it acts faster. It can act anywhere between half an hour to an hour. The problem with it is that users can become physically and psychologically dependent on it when they use it for a few weeks. Hence, you should only use this medication if your symptoms are severe and paralyzing, and nothing else is working for you.
- Antidepressants: Antidepressants can provide you with relief from anxiety, but it doesn't come immediately. You won't feel the full effect until you use it for up to six weeks and above. For some people, antidepressants may not be suitable because it may cause them to have sleep problems, nausea, or other mild side effects. If you notice that you are reacting to any antidepressants prescribed by your qualified mental health expert, inform them

immediately so they can place you on a different product line.

Medication for SAD

The medications that are used for SAD are mostly used as a means to silence symptoms and not cure them altogether. This is the reason it is mostly used with therapy and other self-care practices we've discussed. The belief is that while the medication relieves symptoms, the therapy and self-care processes can help you look for a permanent cure because those ones can address the main cause of the anxiety, not just tackling the symptoms.

A medication commonly prescribed for SAD includes:

- Beta-blockers: This medication relieves performance anxiety. They are used to control the physical symptoms of social anxiety such as shortness of breath, shaky hands or voice, rapid heartbeat, and sweating. However, they cannot affect the emotional symptoms of anxiety. It is typically prescribed for patients with heart disease. A common example of beta-blockers is propranolol (Inderal). To use it, you will have to take it an hour before you encounter a social anxiety trigger such as public speaking. Studies show that it works, as it helps patients perform in the midst of social phobia.

- Benzodiazepines: This medication can also be used for SAD since it is generally an anti-anxiety medication. It works by boosting the activity of gamma-aminobutyric acid (an inhibitory neurotransmitter). In layman terms, it suppresses the signal that travels through the neural pathway. Once these signals are suppressed, the individual experiences a calming of anxiety symptoms. Even though they are fast in action, the problem with them, as we noted before, is that they are sedative and addictive. Hence, they should be used only when other methods have failed.

- Antidepressants: The antidepressants we discussed above can also be useful for SAD, especially when the disorder is very severe.

Medication for OCD

Medication is rarely effective for treating OCD, but some-times antidepressants are prescribed alongside other thera-pies. Medications alone cannot relieve the symptoms. Instead, exposure and response prevention techniques described earlier in this book are mostly used for treating OCD. Cognitive therapy is also used. Cognitive therapy focuses on handling the catastrophic thoughts that cause you the symptoms you feel.

THERAPIES FOR ANXIETY DISORDERS

Therapies are better for anxiety disorders because they uncover the underlying causes of the anxiety you feel. It will help you to learn how to relax and how to look at the situation in a new and less frightening angle. It will also help you develop better coping skills. In summary, therapies equip you with the tools you need to combat anxiety and teach you how to use them.

Anxiety disorders respond well to therapy, and often quickly. The American Psychological Association says that it takes from eight to ten correctly done sessions for people to improve significantly. Therefore, it is mostly a short-term treatment even though it takes longer when compared to medication.

Your therapist will come up with the best plan for you, but two of the most common treatments for anxiety disorders are cognitive behavioral therapy (CBT) and exposure therapy, which focus on the behavior rather than the cause. Most times, the type of anxiety and its severity will determine the treatment approach to be adopted.

These therapies can be conducted for an individual or a group of people—both work.

Cognitive Behavioral Therapy (CBT)

This therapy teaches you some new ways you can start thinking and behaving to reduce or eliminate your anxiety disorder. Fundamentally, it addresses the negative patterns in the way you look at yourself and the world around you. It is these patterns that cause you to have anxiety disorders. It is one of the most effective and widely used treatments for anxiety available. It can be administered by a psychiatrist, psychologist, counselor, or other qualified therapists. It helps you identify and challenge the negative thinking patterns fueling your anxiety.

Several research studies have been done to enquire about the efficacy of CBT as a treatment for anxiety and most of the point to the fact that it is an effective therapy. These studies have discovered that CBT is effective against SAD, GAD, phobias, panic disorders, and many other related illnesses.

From the name "cognitive behavioral therapy," we can see that there are two parts to it, the cognitive part and the behavioral part.

Cognitive therapy is involved with the examination of all the negative thoughts and distortions that you have that cause you anxiety. Behavioral therapy, on the other hand, examines how you behave or react to the objects or situations that trigger your anxiety.

It is our thoughts about an external event that controls our moods, not the external events around us, and that is what CBT is based on. If that is the case, then it is your perception of the situations around you that decides how you feel, not the situations themselves.

Let me demonstrate with this example. If someone invites you for a party with some friends, you may react to it in two broad ways. The first is that you may be happy because parties are fun and you like to meet new people. If you react to the invitation this way, you will be excited and happy. But if you start telling yourself that you don't know how to mingle with people, you don't look presentable enough, and that you will embarrass yourself, the invitation brings you sadness and anxiety.

So you see how different perceptions of an external situation (the invitation) affected your mood in two different ways. It boils down to your attitude and beliefs about situations. If you have anxiety disorders, you will always look at things negatively, and that will fuel your anxiety and fear. CBT, therefore, is targeted at discovering those negative thoughts and correcting them. Once it helps you to change the way you think, you can change the way you feel.

The five components of CBT for anxiety are:

1. Education: As I said earlier, the best point for you to start your fight against any of the anxiety disorders is education. You have to become an expert in that field, and CBT emphasizes that too. CBT teaches that when you understand your anxiety, you will be more accepting and proactive when dealing with it.

2. Monitoring: Once you have educated yourself on your anxiety, the next thing is monitoring the anxiety, discovering your triggers, and noting the intensity of your anxiety with different triggers. With that, you can get a good perspective of your anxiety, and when you start self-care strategies, you can monitor your progress.

3. Physical Control Strategies: Remember how an anxiety disorder gets the better of you by destabilizing you physically, CBT counters that by teaching you relaxation techniques, some of which we discussed in the previous chapter.

4. Cognitive Control Strategies: This aspect of CBT shows you how you can evaluate the thinking pattern that causes you anxiety so that you can begin to alter them. You can alter them by challenging them. As you challenge them, your fears reduce.

5. Behavioral Strategies: CBT teaches you that avoiding the situations you fear is not the best for you; rather, you should summon the courage to tackle them. One way to do that is to imagine the things you fear and put your focus on them. Don't try to escape them. With time, you will become less anxious and gain more control.

The procedure for applying CBT is as follows: identifying a negative thought, challenging the thoughts, and replacing the negative thought with better and realistic thoughts.

For instance, a distortive thought might be: if I climb up that podium to talk to these people, I might pass out. This is you predicting the worst for yourself even when there are other more realistic and better outcomes such as speaking fluently and receiving a standing ovation. You will still tell yourself that if you pass out, it will be a disgrace to you, and people will not take you seriously.

You can replace that negative thought with a more realistic one, such as "I have never passed out on the podium before." You can as well tell yourself that even if you pass out, it will not be so terrible since you will come on soon and you won't be the first person to pass out on a podium.

Your CBT will also help you know when you are beginning to blow things out of proportion so you can return back to more realistic thinking.

Exposure Therapy (ET)

I know how it is much easier to avoid any anxiety-inducing situation because anxiety is not a great thing to feel. So people always try to avoid any situation that can bring them face to face with anxiety. This is why somebody who is scared of flying will prefer to spend several hours on the road to escape their fears. ET helps you to confront your anxieties and fears in a controlled, safe environment. It works on the principle that as you are gradually exposed to your fear (object or situation), either in reality or imagination, your anxiety will start diminishing, and you will gain a greater sense of control over them. That's because as you face the fear and you are not harmed as you thought, you will begin to see how unfounded your fears truly are.

For this therapy, the therapist will ask you to imagine the scary situation, or you may have to confront it. It may be conducted alone or combined with CBT. The therapist will use systematic desensitization when exposing the patient to the anxiety. That will mean starting from small fears and moving to tougher ones. For instance, if you are scared of flying, you may start by looking at photos of planes. After conquering that, you can watch videos of planes in flight, then watch planes as they take off, book a plane ticket, pack for a flight, get on a plane and, eventually, take the flight.

GUIDE FOR APPLICATION OF THERAPIES FOR ANXIETY DISORDERS

As you would expect, some therapies are more effective for some anxiety disorders more than others. Therapies can be used alone or combined with others if need be. Below is a general guide:

- For GAD & SAD, CBT is often used.
- For OCD, a combination of CBT and ERP is often used.
- Sometimes group therapy is recommended, particularly for CBT.

In conclusion, when all the self-help strategies we've discussed have failed, you can fall back to therapy and medication. They can be done differently or combined if there is a need. Whichever one you are going for, ensure that you are doing it with a qualified mental health expert who specializes in anxiety disorders. While the medications will give you faster results, the therapies offer more long-lasting benefits, even though it might take time before you can see notable results.

FINAL WORDS

Anxiety disorders are common mental conditions that are affecting several people daily. It can be challenging for those who have these anxiety disorders. That is because people who suffer from these disorders do not try to understand them. Hence, they are always anxious because they fear what they don't know. But that is not you. You, my friend, have spent time reading this book. My best bet is that you are already beginning to see a glimpse of hope. I want to tell you that if you follow the tips I have shared in this book, you will soon be free from any anxiety disorder that has caged your life.

Now, let's quickly remind ourselves of the talking points so that they can be fresh in your mind as you go all out against that anxiety disorder. We started our discussion by looking at anxiety and the different types of anxiety disorders. I hope you were able to pick the one you have from the lot. We said anxiety, on its own, is normal, but when it starts to interfere with your life and is continuously present, it becomes a disorder. There are seven types of disorder, but three are more common and usually more severe. They include generalized anxiety disorder (GAD), social anxiety disorder (SAD), obsessive-compulsive disorder (OCD), panic disorder, phobias and irrational fears, post-traumatic stress disorder (PTSD), and separation anxiety disorder.

The symptoms of anxiety disorders fall into two broad categories of psychological and physical. They include feelings of dread, expecting the worst, blank mindedness, irritability, difficulty in concentrating for the psychological symptoms and pounding heart, headaches, dizziness, shortness of breath, and so on, for the physical symptoms.

We also took a closer look at anxiety attacks so we can begin to understand why and how they happen. Even though panic attacks and anxiety attacks are somewhat related, they have their differences. Since anxiety attacks can't be medically diagnosed and people living with anxiety often get panic attacks, they are confused for each other. A significant difference between them is that panic attacks are recognized by DSM-5, whereas anxiety attacks are not.

Irrespective of the type of anxiety you may have, certain lifestyle changes can make a significant difference. You have to build your recovery from the disorder on a strong foundation by living a healthy lifestyle. You have to work on your diet because some foods can increase anxiety while some other food can reduce them. You have to add some foods to your diet and also ensure you stick to meal timing. In the same vein, you must eliminate other substances like alcohol and caffeine as they can aggravate symptoms. As you work on your diet, ensure that you often exercise, cut out sources of stress, socialize with people, and get the right amount of sleep.

We also looked at the three major anxiety disorders: GAD, SAD, and OCD. We looked at the symptoms associated with each of them and the coping strategies you can adopt to reduce your symptoms. With most of these anxiety disorders, it is right for you to recognize your triggers and the extent to which they affect you so that you can expect them and act accordingly. While GAD has to do with anxiety and worrying over almost everything, SAD has to do with anxiety when the patient finds themselves in a social setting. OCD is characterized by obsessions and compulsions in which you find yourself doing things even when you know it is illogical. Oftentimes you are doing them because you fear that if you don't, something terrible will happen.

In looking at the self-help strategies you can adopt to fight off anxiety disorders, we looked at emotional freedom technique (EFT), mindfulness, and relaxation technique. EFT is an alternative medicine that is similar to acupuncture. Research shows that it can help you manage stress. Mindfulness enables you to focus your attention on the present so that you can take your mind away from troubling thoughts that cause you anxiety. Relaxation helps you activate the body's relaxation responses so you can better manage anxiety. These self-help techniques have some subdivisions, and we took the time to discuss each one of them. They are mostly things you can do alone except for some that you may need to be taught.

If you've tried self-help strategies and failed, you can try therapy, and if that too fails, you may consider medication. Before going for therapy and medication, check that your symptoms are not due to any underlying medical condition. Once you have ruled that out, have a qualified mental expert take you through therapies and medication. In therapy, your therapist helps you identify the wrong thoughts that cause you anxiety so that you can correct them. Therapy attacks the problem from the root, not just the symptoms. In medication, your therapist prescribes drugs that can ease your symptoms. They are quick, but they can be addictive, making them the last point of call.

I have kept to the promises I made to you. I believe that reading this book has exposed you to the universal truths about anxiety disorders. You have seen that through self-care strategies, you can start to live your life to the fullest again. The best part is that these tips and strategies we've discussed are easy to practice and also very effective. Even if your symptoms are severe, I have provided you with a guide on medication and therapy. With this, you are equipped with all the knowledge you need to be free again.

My final piece of advice is that you should start seeing this as doable. You may know all the strategies that can help you, but if you don't think they will work, you will not put in the efforts that will make them work. Again, you know how effective recovery from anxiety disorders might warrant you to expose yourself to those things you fear most. Do not hesitate to do it. Find the courage to do it and reap long-term rewards.

If you can leave a favorable review, you can help me get these tips and strategies out to people who need it to be free from their fears. Thank you, and I hope you enjoyed my work.

Best wishes!

Made in the USA
Monee, IL
13 January 2021

57445202R00100